D1584617

BASICS

A BEGINNER'S GUIDE TO STAGE LIGHTING

Peter Coleman

ENTERTAINMENT TECHNOLOGY PRESS

Educational Series

Illustrations by Jackie Staines

BASICS
A BEGINNER'S GUIDE TO STAGE LIGHTING

Peter Coleman

Entertainment Technology Press

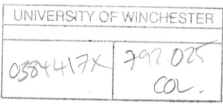

Basics

A Beginner's Guide to Stage Lighting

© Peter Coleman

First edition Published August 2003 by
Entertainment Technology Press Ltd
The Studio, High Green, Great Shelford, Cambridge, CB22 5EG
Internet: www.etnow.com

ISBN 1 904031 20 X

A title within the
Entertainment Technology Press Educational Series
Series editor: John Offord

CODE / BAS001

CONTENTS

INTRODUCTION

As with so many things, the last years of the 20th century saw us all having to learn at a frantic speed just to keep pace with the latest technology available. It's a sobering thought that I was still working a resistance 'Grand Master' dimmer system in one of the UK's major touring venues, while mankind was landing on the moon. But I am now specifying computer control systems for use in schools!

People who know me will tell you that faced with a new piece of technical equipment I rarely, if ever, read the instruction manual before I try to use it! But I make a plea for you not to skip over this introduction because it may give you some insight into what this book is about.

Over the last 30 years plus I have been involved with the technical side of performing arts, or as I prefer to think of it 'The Theatre'. My family were all part of it - grandparents, parents, sister, uncles, cousins - so it was natural that when I started work it would be my chosen profession. (My parents did somewhat half heartedly try to steer me away from the theatre but to no avail.)

Without wishing to sound too old, when I started working in theatre there simply was no external or educational training available for the technical areas. Yes, you could train and become a qualified electrician and drama schools have always run semi-technical elements within their stage management courses. But in the main, until quite recently there was nowhere to learn the technical side of theatre other than by real live on-the-job experience.

So from the age of about 15 when I started 'officially' part time as a follow spot operator (the place had been my second home from as early as I can remember), I gradually learnt the technical theatre trade, mainly based upon lighting. However, in my 'nursery' of The Grand Theatre in Wolverhampton, the major part of the year, some 20 weeks, were spent in weekly rep and as you can perhaps imagine, everybody had to have some ability in every technical area. Carrying barrels of beer to the upper circle bar was stretching it a bit, but then somebody had to do that too.

Perhaps it's because I am a slow learner, or perhaps I was just enjoying myself too much working in live performance theatre, but one day several theatre jobs later, feeling frustrated at having to deal with another sales rep from a lighting company, it dawned upon me that I actually knew far more about the product that was being offered than the salesman who was trying to sell it to me!

Not long after this startling realisation I decided to give up the real end-product job. There would be no more finishing work at 10.30 every night, no more all-night fit ups, no more cold and wet get-outs, no more - well lots of other things which went with the job (and still do for those still doing it). I decided instead to put my knowledge and experience to work for me, and instead of doing it, I started selling it!

Well, things move on, and gradually, while still actively involved in selling technical product, my roll has changed to: Advisor? Teacher? Lecturer? Specifier? Lighting Expert? Well, it's a combination of all these plus a few more. In fact, the job which is now the 'day job' has me titled as Design Consultant - rather grand, but then what's in a name?

So what am I doing writing this? Well, it's a bit like me feeling miffed at that sales rep I mentioned earlier. I seem to spend a lot of time talking and explaining the do's and don'ts and the technical mysteries to all sorts of people who usually ask: "where can I get a reference book which will tell me all this?"

Now I know there are quite a few very good reference works available, but I have found that in the main these assume rather too much of the reader and can sometimes get very involved. Worse still, they don't give the reader the *BASIC* information. Not that I disagree with much that is written, but rather that I feel I can do better! You, the reader, will have to be the judge of that!

Anyway, it will probably do me good to get it off my chest, and I trust you will forgive the style, which may tend to ramble! Some of my colleagues and a fair number of my customers tell me that once I start on a topic near to my heart it's difficult to shut me up. So if you get fed up, the book will close!

So who is this book aimed at? Really the beginner, someone who needs some of the mysteries explained, or perhaps for those of you who find that the technical side of the performing arts just isn't working for you in your own application.

I hope I have managed to explain things in easy-to-understand terms. There are a few areas which may need a little thought and extra study, and of course there may even be one or two contentious points. But in the main I hope you find the book both helpful and useful.

"If you get six different Lighting Designers/Theatre Technicians or even Design Consultants giving a view on how or why to do something in a particular way, you are likely to get six different answers." I find myself saying this to lots of people, so although it's a rather long-winded statement I suppose it could be this book's alternative title.

It's not a 'story', neither is it a real 'reference work'. It's not intended to be the complete and finished article giving specific answers to all your questions. It is just about *BASICS*.

I feel as if most sections of this book should look a little like my tax return, where it says, if you have ticked (a) then move to page 29 and look at section (7b) because I know a good many of you will not want to wade your way through things which you may consider are not relevant to you.

Of course, you can skip over various sections, but you may miss something that just might help it all make sense.

PROLOGUE

I suggest that in whichever discipline of the technical performance arts you are interested in, the first thing you will need to know is what 'tools' you will need to do the job in hand.

In the performance lighting business the tools are first and foremost the lanterns. Part 1 will start to explain the difference between the various lantern types. For those of you who are already familiar with these tools the descriptions may seem rather unnecessary, but as I have said before, this book is aimed at the beginner - who may not fully appreciate what the differences are and how and why they are important.

And I must labour the point here. While we all accept and applaud the advance in technology that has brought us so much marvellous equipment to make the lighting job easier and better, there is one principle fact that you will keep returning to. Despite computer control, digital dimming, moving lights, colour scrollers, Ethernet driven systems and information, your work will in most cases come down to a selection of strategically placed fixed lanterns, from which light can be directed onto the performance area.

It's this very *BASIC* element of the job, plus a few important peripherals, such as dimmers, control and rigging, that I am trying to help you with.

The family of lanterns which are described in the following sections offer the five main categories, or types of lantern which you will find in common use. There are a few derivatives, such as beamlights, light curtains, projectors, followspots and others - but don't worry too much about them just yet because in the main they are effects lanterns which do very specific jobs.

Having got the equipment out of the way, you may expect that the next element of the job in in the design. Sorry to disappoint you here – I find the prospect of writing the 'how to do' of lighting design rather daunting and like trying to write a book about how to drive a car for the non-driver. You can see how it would all get written down and make perfect sense, but be next to useless at the same time. No, I feel the best plan is to give you some of the important nuts and bolts information, then you can add your own design to it, budgets and time permitting of course!

1 LANTERNS

The Flood

The flood is the simplest form of lantern, usually an enclosure with one open side, a reflector and a light source. Modern flood lanterns will accept colour filter and may also be fitted with a 'barndoor' unit, although due to the nature of the light output from the flood this option has limited use.

The flood is normally regarded as an area lighting device, not specifically used for lighting people. It will operate as any other type of lantern, having a yoke providing a suspension point and so it can adjusted to 'pan' and 'tilt'.

Any form of light source with an open front (no lens) may be regarded as a flood. In older installations the 'footlights' are floods and when positioned above the stage area are refereed to as 'battens'.

Older flood lanterns will use various types of lamps ranging from 150W to 1000W, which are normally of an older domestic style. Smaller venues will often have an abundance of flood lanterns and are thus forced to use them to light the performance area because they are the only type of lantern that is available! This is unfortunate since the flood offers little to the overall 'lighting', save that the whole area is brighter.

The modern flood will probably use a linear tungsten halogen lamp, but it remains an area lighting tool, better designed but still having limited ability.

But the flood is non-the-less a useful tool when used in the right place. It's invaluable for the broad wash of light needed to cover a cyclorama cloth or a door backing. Most end stage performance lighting will call for the lighting of a cyclorama or backcloth, so the flood, probably in multiples, will almost certainly be a requirement.

It may seem odd to start thinking of your

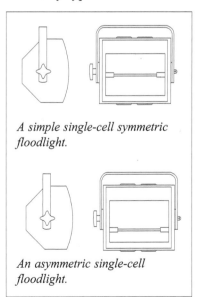

A simple single-cell symmetric floodlight.

An asymmetric single-cell floodlight.

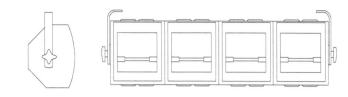

A four-cell in-line cyclorama flood. Each cell is individually wired to enable four independently controllable colour washes.

lighting design with what is after all probably the last, and you may think the least significant, piece of equipment that you are likely to use. Well not really. Consider the specific reasons why the cyclorama flood is needed.

1. To provide a coverage of light in probably three or four colours (modern floods work in multiple units) to enhance a painted image or to colour a plain cloth.
2. To eliminate the spill and shadows on a cyclorama cloth, caused by the other lanterns lighting the performance area.

In either case, without the flood the cyclorama, backcloth, back wall, or whatever forms the rear of the performance space, would look very odd.

One major new innovation in the flood is the asymmetric reflector. This gives a light intensity bias to the output of the light, and when positioned at the top of a cloth the flood will output its most intense (brightest) light towards the bottom of the cloth, the overall result being a more even distribution of light. Likewise, in reverse, when it is used on the floor as a 'ground row'.

The complete cyclorama lighting effect will often use both top and bottom lighting and depending upon the material used may be either front or back lit.

The Fresnel

The Fresnel lantern takes its name from the inventor of the lens - Augustin-Jean Fresnel – born 10th May 1788 in Broglie - France, died 14th July 1827. Although Fresnel was not the first to experiment with dividing the lens surface into concentric rings, originally to save weight while giving a concentrated beam with a short focal length, the Fresnel design was probably the first lens of its type put to common use. It is still used on very large scale in lighthouses and eventually found its way into many different types of light fittings, including theatrical lantern application.

The Fresnel lens gives a variable soft edge light output to your lantern, and when used in multiples helps to produce a continuous area coverage. The light output is controllable, being varied from a small intense spot to a wide or flood (not to be confused with the flood lantern) coverage. This control is a part of the 'focus' process, focus being the ability to increase and decrease the size of the 'spot' or light output from the lantern. This is achieved by

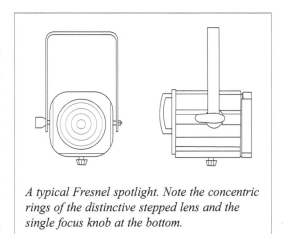

A typical Fresnel spotlight. Note the concentric rings of the distinctive stepped lens and the single focus knob at the bottom.

moving the lamp forwards of backwards in relation to the fixed lens. The nearer the lamp is to the lens the wider/larger the output, and correspondingly the further the lamp is away from the lens, the narrower/smaller the light output.

This range of movement will differ from model to model, some using a rather crude sliding tray mechanism made easier in recent years with the addition of PTFE strips or washers. Some models will have a worm screw gear permitting the operator to wind the lamp and reflector backwards and forwards within the body of the lantern.

Colour can be used in a frame fitted into colour frame runners/holders at the front of the lantern. The lantern yoke provides a suspension/pivot point thus pan and tilt can be achieved. A barndoor attachment is often used with a Fresnel lantern, and this helps to keep the spill and scatter (unwanted peripheral light) to an acceptable level.

Fresnel lanterns are available in a range of sizes (Wattage) from 300W through 500W, 650W, 1kW and 1.2kW - all commonly found in live performance use. Up to 2.5kW, 5kW and even 10kW are used in film and TV lighting. The light source is either the traditional tungsten halogen filament lamp or a discharge (non-filament arc lamp) for film and TV work.

The Profile

The profile lantern will have one or more plain convex lenses and the ability to provide a light output having a sharp/hard-defined edge. The modern profile,

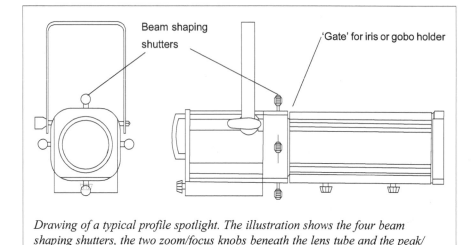

Drawing of a typical profile spotlight. The illustration shows the four beam shaping shutters, the two zoom/focus knobs beneath the lens tube and the peak/field adjustment on the rear of the lamphouse.

sometimes called a 'zoom profile', will have two lenses. This provides the advantage that while one lens will alter the focal length, making the light output larger or smaller, the other lens will control the 'focus' - making the edge of the beam either hard or soft. While never as soft or diffused as a Fresnel lens lantern, this ability is very useful as a hard defined edge is not always required.

Of course, profile lanterns will accept colour filter in a frame fitted into colour frame runners/holders at the front of the lantern. It is not normal to use a barndoor attachment with a profile since the lantern does not produce as much 'spill' and 'scatter' as seen in the Fresnel lantern and beam shaping is provided by a set of 'shutter' blades, which allow precise light shapes to be created.

The lantern yoke provides a suspension/pivot point, so pan and tilt can be achieved. Some larger profile lanterns will have an adjustable position for the yoke assembly, permitting suspension from different positions along the length of the lantern. This is specially useful when lanterns are to be suspended in inaccessible places, or where they may be in conflict with other structures such as the circle front of a theatre auditorium.

Profile lanterns are available in a range of sizes (Wattage) from 650W through 1kW, 1.2kW, 2kW and 2.5kW - and all are commonly found in live performance use. The profile lantern has less appeal/use in larger sizes and unlike the Fresnel, which just gets bigger as it is used in film and TV lighting, the profile is not greatly used in this sector.

Profile lanterns are often described with numbers, e.g. 16-30, 15-32, 23-50. These refer to the beam angle of the lantern and two numbers indicate that the lantern has a variable range such as 16 to 30 degrees.

Imagine a line extending from the centre of the lantern along its long axis (in the direction in which the light travels). The light output is variable from 16 degrees (minimum) to 30 degrees (maximum) using the imaginary line as the centre point. This movement is achieved by moving the lenses which are mounted in a 'carrier' within the 'lens tube' (front end of the lantern). So, by moving lens carrier forwards and backwards within the lens tube you change the angle and the size and focus of the light output.

Modern profile lanterns will contain a set of shutters (usually four) blades which are introduced into the light path before the lens. The adjustment/use of the shutter blades allows the beam to be shaped, a feature which can be very precise and much used in focusing profile lanterns into specific areas or to light specific objects.

Most profile lanterns will have a slot or gate behind the lenses at the same position as the shutter blades. This can be used to hold an 'iris diaphragm', a multi-leaf circular device which gives the user the ability to close the aperture (thus the light source), making the light output image instantly variable.

The gate will also accept a gobo (a small metal plate etched with a pattern), turning the profile lantern into a form of projector.

Within the lamp house (rear of the lantern) the lamp will be mounted in front of or surrounded by a semi-circular reflector. For certain applications such as the use of a gobo, it is desirable that the light output of the lantern is spread evenly across the whole of the image, whereas in other applications a central 'hot spot' may be needed. This is achieved by a lamp adjustment control (knob) located at the bottom/rear of the lantern. The action of this control provides what is called 'flat field' or 'peak' adjustment and is set as required.

Recent advances in lamp technology, coupled with similar advances in lens and reflector manufacture, have added the axial lamp, the cold mirror reflector and the condenser lens. More of these later, but they all add to the performance of the profile lantern.

The Followspot

The followspot is simply a profile lantern, usually of large capacity, with an

integral iris diaphragm, blackout shutters, a colour magazine and operator handles and controls. It is normally a narrow angle focus range lantern, as it usually operates over a longer distance (throw) than other lanterns and by the nature of what it needs to do has a need to produce a small concentrated image.

The modern followspot will often differ in one major respect from a normal profile. Whereas a filament lamp is used in a normal profile, the followspot may use a discharge (enclosed arc) lamp. This type of lamp gives a much brighter light output in proportion to its rated wattage e.g. a 1.2kW HMI (Halide Metal Iodide) would be approximately twice as bright as a 2kW tungsten halogen filament lamp. This difference apart, the followspot is just another profile lantern but designed to work with hands-on operation.

A Typical followspot set up on a stand for manual operation. Note the external ballast containing the large choke and special electronics required to 'strike' a discharge lamp.

The Prism Convex

Very similar in external appearance to the Fresnel, this lantern uses a prism convex lens, providing a semi hard/soft edge to the light output. Softer than a profile lantern, but more defined than a Fresnel, it is often used with a barndoor attachment providing control of unwanted light spill and scatter. Like the Fresnel it will have a focus control providing a small and almost parallel beam of light adjusting to a wide or flood (not to be confused with the flood lantern) coverage.

Colour can be used in a frame fitted into colour frame runners/holders at the front of the lantern. The lantern yoke provides a suspension/pivot point so pan and tilt can be achieved.

Prism convex lanterns are available in a range of sizes (Wattage) from 500W through 650W, 1kW and 1.2kW up to 2kW and 2.5kW - all commonly found in live performance use. The prism convex lantern is rarely found in film TV and studio lighting use.

Known as the PC for short, the prism convex lantern has a rather odd pedigree, in that some of the first 'lanterns' which advanced from the flood had a similar light output. These lanterns were in fact not PC's at all but single lens profile lanterns. Then, for quite a number of years, this type of lantern was discarded in favour of the now more traditional profile lantern with two, often moveable (zoom) lenses, which provided a much cleaner image.

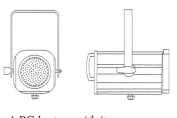

A PC lantern with its characteristic 'pebbled' lens. The knob on the bottom moves the lamp and reflector assembly closer to or further from the lens to change the beam angle from wide flood to tight spot.

The modern PC lantern re-emerged in the 1980s with its prism convex lens, not just a single profile (plain convex) lens, but slightly different in that the rear flat face of the lens has a rough (dimpled) surface. The effect of this on the light output is to provide a more defined edge to the spot than a Fresnel lens. Some people regard this as an intermediate lantern – not as soft as the Fresnel and without the spill and scatter, but not as hard as the profile.

Its specific use/position is a little hard to define, but it's probably nearer to the Fresnel than the profile. Some designers speculate that in time the PC will be more numerous than the Fresnel and be used and specified far more; others will happily continue to use their Fresnels and not be too bothered about it at all.

The PAR Lantern

The PAR (Parabolic Aluminised Reflector) lantern has many size variants. In its largest form (PAR 64) it has properties which are hard to reproduce with other lantern types. It is really a one-off, and combines very high light output with light weight and relatively low cost.

The numbers (64 - 38 - 56 etc) associated with PAR lanterns are the number of $1/8$ inch of the diameter of the lamp front. The traditional lantern yoke providing pan and tilt is supplemented in the 'floor can' with a double yoke providing a free standing floor mounted unit, usually in the form of a 'short nose' body and usually used with a wide angle lamp for short throw applications.

Colour is used in a normal colour frame fitted in runners/holders at the front

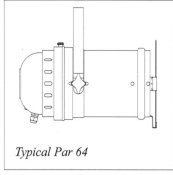
Typical Par 64

of the lantern but due to the high output of the lamp used, colour 'burn out' is common.

The PAR lantern, often called the Par 'Can' or the Sealed Beam Reflector, is unlike all of the other lantern types because the Par lamp is really 50% of the lantern. This is normally a sealed beam unit looking a little like a large car headlamp, although there are some variants known as 'ray lights' which use a reflector with an integral lamp holder and separate lamp. The Par lamp is the most common.

The rock and roll music industry was the first to see the advantages of the Par lamp but over the years the more traditional theatre/arts performance related users have made much use of it. Perhaps the most striking feature of the Par lamp is its very high light output. In all its many sizes, from the small Par 16 to the largest Par 64, it gives a very high light output.

The smaller Par lamps, 16 and 36, are a low voltage type and are used with a transformer; this may be housed within a part of the lantern fitting or may be externally sited. The larger Par lamps, 56 and 64, are normally 230V rated. However, they are also used at 120V where two lamps (lanterns) will be used wired in series for 230V operation. You should be aware of this voltage variant, and if using unfamiliar equipment check the lamp operating voltage!

The light output from a Par lamp is fixed, so unlike most other lantern types you cannot change or vary the shape of the light output/beam. The output is not a regular circle or spot, it is oval/ellipse shape and while you cannot change this you can rotate the whole lamp within the lantern, thus tuning the ellipse to either an upright or a flat position.

Because no variation in focus possible, lamp manufacturers have solved this problem by making a range of lamps with different front/lenses of the basic sealed beam light source. So, in current regular use you will find narrow, medium and wide-angle lamp types.

The medium angle (CP61) is the most commonly used Par lamp in the Par 64 range while the wide angle (CP62) is often used in what are known as 'short nose' or 'floor' cans. The narrow angle lamp (CP60) is ideal for use over long distances (30m+) but does not perform well over short distances.

The 120V versions of Par lamps are available in five or six grades or angles, mainly at the narrow angle end of the range.

The Par lantern (Par 64) is extremely light, weighing less than 4kgs, compared, for example, to a 1.2kW Profile lantern at about 13kgs.

Because of its high light output it is very effective when used with deep saturated colours. Modern technology is now using multiple Par lamps within one housing – not a lantern in the traditional sense rather a 'bank' of lamps combined together in quantities of 6, 8 or 12.

The most recent addition to the family of Par lanterns is not a true Par lantern at all. The Source Four PAR (from American manufacturer ETC) does not use a standard sealed beam PAR lamp, but a more traditional reflector - not unlike the ray light and a standard axial filament lamp. Another major step forward with this lantern is the use of multiple (four) different lens fronts, making it easy to change from wide to narrow angle without changing the lamp.

Accessories

Within the five lantern type sections discussed above various accessories have been mentioned. By way of clarification, these are described below.

The *barndoor* is an attachment which clips onto the front of a Fresnel, PC or sometimes a Par lantern. It has four adjustable panels which are hinged to the frame so that they may be set individually as required, the whole frame being able to rotate through 360 degrees around the front of the lantern, providing the ability to use the chosen barndoor or doors at the angle of your choice.

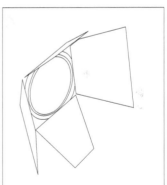

The *iris diaphragm* is a device made up of multiple metal strips or leaves with one operating handle to open or close the iris. The iris is used only with profile lanterns and adds a more variable control than the lens adjustment over the size of the light output/ spot. It is used/positioned between the lamp and the lenses, fitting into a ready-made slot called the lantern 'gate'.

Gobos and *gobo holders* are used only with profile lanterns, and are widely used to create images/projections. A wide selection - many

Barndoor attachments slot on to the front of Fresnels and PCs to control the shape and spill of the beam. Barndoors are also sometimes used on Parcans and floods.

thousands - are available from stock ranges from various manufacturers. They are positioned between the lamp and the lens, fitting into the lantern gate.

As the name implies, a *colour frame* is simply a metal or fibre frame which will contain the colour of your choice. It is worth mentioning that the modern ranges of colour filter, which are now all high temperature and self extinguishing, need to be sandwiched into the frame – the sides, top and bottom gripping the colour filter. Older lantern types may have colour frames with metal wires in place, but this type of frame was designed for use with a range/type of colour filter now long discontinued. You may well find that if you use this type of colour frame with new high temperature filter it will actually cause the filter to burn out where it comes into contact with the wires.

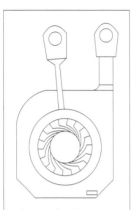

An iris diaphragm used for altering the aperture (and therefore beam) size of a profile lantern.

Not receiving a specific mention within the lantern descriptions, but a definite requirement nonetheless is the *hook clamp* and the *safety bond*. The hook clamp, sometimes called the 'G' clamp, is used where the lantern is to be suspended from a bar (probably about 90% of the time). The standard clamp is made to fit onto a 48/50mm ($1^7/_8$ / 2") bar and has a wing bolt passing through it which allows you to 'clamp' the lantern tight onto the bar. (This is a very important factor, and the section on focusing the lantern (see page 30) will say more about this.) The hook clamp is generally a 'one size fits all' device, until you get through to the larger 2kW and TV specification lanterns, where a bigger and more substantial piece of metalwork is required.

An important aspect about the humble hook clamp which many people get wrong concerns its fixing to the lantern. The lantern will have a nut and bolt passing through the yoke (sometimes called the trunion arm) at the centre point. This nut and bolt should have at least one flat washer and one spring washer and the important thing to remember is to

A 'break-up' gobo in a gobo holder.

place one flat washer between the yoke of the lantern and the hook clamp, so that the act of panning the lantern (swivelling it left and right during the focus process - *more later*) will provide a small pivotal area, and not allow the whole of the underside of the hook clamp to come into contact with the top of the lantern yoke.

Again, with reference to the 'focus' process, you should make sure that the nut associated to the bolt securing the hook clamp is in good condition. This may sound rather silly: what could be wrong with a nut, and why is it even worth a mention? Well, there are two main types, the older 'wing' nut designed to be tightened with your fingers, and the more common modern hexagonal nut, requiring a spanner to tighten it. The older 'wing' nut can often be found, minus one or even both wings! Not a lot of use! The 'hex' nut can sometimes be so well used that the corners are rounded off, making it very difficult to tighten, as the spanner will keep slipping off. All of this makes the 'locking off' process within the 'focusing' job a real nightmare.

Finally, there's the safety bond. Until quite recently we've all used safety chains, but Health & Safety legislation has seen the chain downgraded. The word 'safety' is now only applicable to a steel wire 'bond'. Whichever you use, it is there to provide a secondary means of suspension, just in case that nut and bolt should come undone. Modern lantern ranges will usually have a safety anchor point built into the body of the lantern. However, older types will not have this facility and you will then simply pass the bond through the lantern yoke. In each case the bond will then pass over the bar from which the lantern is suspended.

As with the simple hook clamp and its nut and bolt arrangement, there is a right and wrong way to fit a safety bond. When rigging the lantern on the bar, don't wrap the slack bond wire or chain around and around the bar making a tight connection between the bar and lantern as it will be impossible to focus the lantern when the time comes. Simply make the connection of the bond or chain leaving as much slack as possible, allowing the lantern to pan and tilt without any restriction from the bond.

Lamps

A few words on lamps. By the way, lamps go into lanterns, bulbs go into your garden!

Almost all the lamp types you are likely to come into contact with, used in the basic ranges of lanterns, will be tungsten halogen. The lamp filament is made of a tungsten material, just the same as with domestic style lamps, but this is surrounded/enclosed not by a vacuum like the domestic types, but by a halogen gas. As the tungsten filament heats up it will in time deteriorate/discolour. The halogen gas acts as a cleaning agent, helping to keep the filament in good condition for as long as possible.

As with all other technological advances in recent years, the modern tungsten halogen lamp has now evolved into quite a robust piece of engineering (not so in the early days) and you should achieve at least the manufacturer's recommendation for burning hours/lamp life. This is usually between 300 and 750 hours, depending upon the type.

For many users the costs involved in new/replacement lamps is a major factor, for although the technology has kept the costs to a sensible level, they are still one of the more expensive consumables you will use. In order to maximise the life expectancy of your tungsten halogen lamps, there are one or two golden rules which will help.

The linear tungsten halogen lamp used in most modern floods is designed to work only in the horizontal, so don't be tempted to operate your flood on its side, as premature failure will result.

Leaving aside the PAR lamp, about 75% of the remaining lamp types are designed to work in what is known as 'base-down' mode, as you would expect with the base (or cap) of the lamp at the bottom. All these lamps are designed to work at + or - 90 degrees from the vertical. If you tilt the lamp further passed 90 degrees so that the filament is below the level of the base, you will cause premature failure.

So what of the other 25% of lamp types and how do you tell which is which? Well the next 24% are probably in the category of axial style lamps. Unlike base-down lamps, the axials have a filament which is designed to operate pointing in a straight line down the lens tube of the lantern, in the direction in which the light travels. This, as you can imagine, requires the lamp to operate with its base or cap above the level of the filament, contrary to the rules for using the base-down type lamps. The axial is a very efficient lamp and the lanterns which use them have half spherical, often dichroic glass reflectors. The whole package usually results in a lamp with a Wattage of say 600W, being equal or brighter than a comparable upright filament lamp of twice the Wattage.

That just leaves the remaining 1%, and there always has to be an exception to the rule, doesn't there? There is still in existence, albeit now long

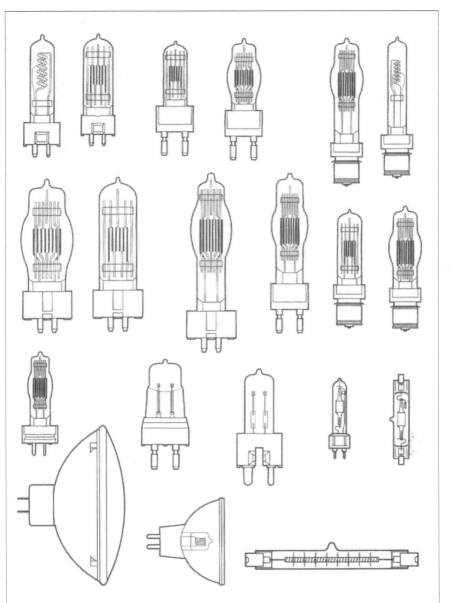

A sample of specialist lamps found in theatres and entertainment venues. Note the different base types, filament structures and envelope shapes and sizes. Drawings courtesy GE Lighting.

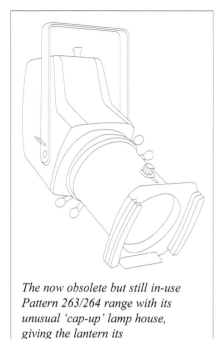

The now obsolete but still in-use Pattern 263/264 range with its unusual 'cap-up' lamp house, giving the lantern its characteristic 'banana' shape.

discontinued, a range of lanterns named 263 and 264 which use a lamp that is designed to operate base or cap up not down! They use a lamp called the T15 or T23, and just to complicate matters even further, many users have converted these lanterns to take a standard base-down lamp. What a mess! If in doubt, ask someone who knows.

The larger PAR lamps are yet another tungsten halogen lamp type but this time the lamp is enclosed in a sealed beam unit, the orientation of which is less critical than the other types of lamp.

The standard lantern types will probably use one of the lamp types described; the only other exception will probably be followspots which in the larger sizes may use a discharge lamp. There are a number of different types of discharge lamp, the most common being CSI (compact source iodide), HMI (halide metal iodide) and MSR (medium source rare-earth). The main feature about these lamp types that you will notice - apart from their high cost - is that they do not have a filament, so don't throw them away thinking they have blown! They work by a very high voltage being passed across the two internal pillars (electrodes) within the lamp, causing a sustained arc of light.

It is worth noting here that this type of lamp/lantern is never used with a dimmer. It simply won't work and likely as not will damage the dimmer. This discharge type lamp just needs a power supply and the lanterns will probably have an external 'ballast' unit, which generates the very high voltages required to first 'strike' the lamp and then keep it running.

Many discharge lamp types used in followspots, will not re-strike (start) if they are hot and may need up to 15 - 20 minutes to cool down before they will be useable again. The golden rule here is, don't turn the thing off unless you know it will be out of use for some time.

This brings into discussion a particular problem associated with followspots. If you don't turn them off, you may be forced to keep them 'blacked out' by using the blackout shutter or iris. This is fine if the blackout is a metal blade shutter mechanism, but if it's combined with the iris and if you hold the blackout in place for too long (over one minute is probably too long), you will effectively 'cook' the iris and the overheating will distort its leaves to a point where it will be at best very stiff and at worst totally unuseable. Most good followspots will have a mechanical plate shutter behind, and in addition to the iris, so the use of both will prevent the problem. However, if you are using a followspot with only a blackout iris, you should use a piece of blackout material (thin tin plate is good but anything flammable is not), placed into one of the colour magazine slots. That way you can blackout the followspot without overheating the iris.

I seem to have rambled away from accessories and lamps in particular, but where lamps are concerned, the subject of handling them is yet another important factor. Although there are still a few exceptions (non tungsten halogen general service lamps), the vast majority should not be handled unless you are wearing protective gloves, for no matter how clean your hands may be, the natural oils from your skin will burn onto and through the 'fused quartz envelope' and very soon discolour it, affecting the operation of the halogen cycle within. And here you are thinking: "I didn't know I had a fused quartz envelope, let alone a halogen cycle". But don't worry, it's just the manufacturers' posh name for glass and the cleaning action of the gas in-fill.

A further note of caution is needed here. When you are replacing any failed lamp, and specially Tungsten Halogen types which run at very high temperatures. You should first un-plug the lantern from the power supply (dimmer) and make sure that the lamp has cooled sufficiently, to permit safe handling. You may also occasionally experience a lamp failure where the lamp has suffered a complete mechanical failure, with fragments of glass scattered all over the inside of the lantern. Although this is very rare, when it happens you should take the lantern out of use and give it a thorough clean, to remove all of the glass fragments, before putting it back into use.

Nonetheless, handling your lamps incorrectly can be another cause of premature failure, so beware and take note of the manufacturer's instructions on the lamp carton or printed on an enclosed sheet. Most will even provide a glove or protective cover (which you must remember to remove once you have installed the lamp).

Lanterns: Why so many different types - and where and how to use them

A good question, often asked by the beginner, regarding the five categories listed earlier - flood, Fresnel, profile, prism convex and PAR – is why so many different types, and where and how to use them. Well, it's pretty obvious that the flood has some fundamental uses which the other types can't achieve. Remember, I described it as "an area, not a people lighter". But with the other four, maybe the differences are not quite so obvious.

Let's single out the profile range. They have one major advantage over all the others, and I don't mean gobo projection. That's far too simple. It's the fact that the lens system in a profile lantern puts all of the available light in a very defined and controllable area with the minimum amount of spill and scatter. To understand how and why this is important we need to consider the wider requirements of a performance in front of a live audience and to do this we even have to become a little 'artistic'.

This is the first of a number of in-the-field scenarios which I hope may explain where I'm coming from and help you get to where you are going.

In a traditional end stage environment, large or small, the audience is seated looking at the performers on stage. The stage is usually raised and bounded by the proscenium arch, so the audience is effectively looking at the performers contained within a box or rectangle at one end of a large room. Think of it as a version of the TV in your lounge at home, and keeping that picture in mind, consider why it is that when you see a good film on TV it's still never as good as when you see it on the big screen in a cinema? Well, the sound is better and there are fewer distractions like advertisements, other people coming and going etc. etc. Yes, true – but one major factor is the physical size of the screen images, considerably bigger than you get at home, even with a big TV set! So how and why is this relevant to the stage lighting? It's all a matter of illusion and a feeling of intimate contact or closeness to the performers.

The cinema screen achieves this with bigger than life-size images. Unfortunately, in live theatre the effect is not available and being stuck with people at actual size we then do the reverse of the cinematic illusion. We downsize the people by putting them in a picture frame image at one end of our large room, and the effect is to distance the performer from the audience.

For certain live performance works this effect is less relevant than for others. Generally, anything which is light-hearted – comedy, pantomime, musical etc. – is not too concerned about 'the box on the wall' effect because the very nature of the performance will, as the old expression goes, 'get over the footlights'. But for the more serious dramatic works where the performance is a little more wordy and less raucous, that 'box on the wall' can be a real problem. Of course, on the larger theatrical performance scale of things people and planners put specific types of performance into specific buildings. You may well go to The London Palladium to see a pantomime but would you expect to go to the same venue to see Richard III. I expect not!

But I still haven't said how lighting and specific lanterns can have any relevance to this effect. Well, it's all down to that box on the wall and lighting it, or actually not lighting it!

If the performer is distanced from the audience by being put into a picture frame, then simple - don't put them in a picture frame! But that's not so simple, as you can't take the picture frame away - it's a part of the building structure. But what you don't do is light it, or don't draw attention to it. Don't highlight the feature which is the picture frame. If possible, get it painted black! Then you will succeed to some degree in removing the distance effect between the performer and the audience.

Some would say that if the performance was good enough it would carry the intimacy direct to every seat in the house without the need to worry about such trivia as to whether the proscenium arch was lit or not. I couldn't possibly comment - except to say that I've seen some performances where the proscenium arch not only had a supporting role but was the best thing in the show!

Back to lantern types and uses and our profile range of lanterns. Because of the lens system involved there is very little unwanted light coming out of the front of your profile lantern and by some adept work with the beam shaping shutters you should be able to light right up the very edge of the proscenium arch without getting light all over it. So we have another specific use for one of our lantern types: any lantern position actually within the auditorium, commonly referred to as FOH (Front of House).

Yes, of course you can use the profile lantern in other places, over stage, side stage, stage or fly rail booms or ladders, as area lighting or for gobo projection, and not forgetting followspots. They are perhaps the most versatile of lanterns but then they are also one of the most expensive, being on average more than twice the cost of a Fresnel or prism convex lantern of a similar Wattage/size.

Lets consider the PAR can range of lanterns next. More than once I make reference to general rules and exceptions to them. The PAR 'can' (I shall now stop calling it a lantern and refer to it as it is generically named), breaks quite a few of the rules, and as with all tools, once you know what you can and cannot do with them, their use becomes much easier.

In its larger formats (PAR 64 and 56), it is very good at getting a lot of light into a relatively small area with very good results in dense colour wash applications, and it's physically lighter and much cheaper than other lanterns of its Wattage/size. It's not good for precise focus work because it's not easily variable like the profile, Fresnel or prism convex - and it may well burn out those dense saturated colours which it performs so well with.

The PAR is used just about everywhere and often in multiples. It's very affective where a strong back light is needed over stage, but is equally well used to stripe a skyscape backcloth or provide dress lighting for FOH tabs. It can be used in its floor mounting double yoke form as a 'shin buster' on side stage to light dance, or around the drum riser for your rock band.

As I said: "Once you know what it will do, so use it and love it". The PAR is a very cost effective way of lighting your performance space, but you will need some of the other lantern types if your need is for the more traditional style of performance lighting.

I will combine the function of the Fresnel and prism convex lanterns here and describe them as 'acting area coverage lanterns'. Both types operate in a similar way, with similar focus/coverage abilities. It really is only the lens and thus the extremity/edge of the spot which differs. But both are used in multiples to achieve area lighting coverage. They are often used with a barndoor attachment to help cut down on the unwanted spill and scatter that is present with all lanterns of this type.

The prism convex (from now on referred to by its generic name, PC) is helped a great deal by the use of the barndoor – more so than the Fresnel – and indeed to a point where it can approach the ability of a shuttered profile lantern. It can never match it, but for some applications this ability may prove very useful.

Fresnels and PCs will be found in all over-stage positions, and taken together are probably the most numerous in the toolbox of lanterns found in a performance lighting space.

Their exact use can be best demonstrated within the next section, because now having a general idea of the tools at your disposal you need to progress to perhaps the most crucial part of performance lighting.

Focusing your lanterns – The Lighting Coverage

With the advent of a lantern with a specific output (spot) rather than a flood comes the need for numbers of lanterns to be used together, often making what is referred to as a coverage or 'wash' of light. The art of making a good coverage is perceived by some to be simple and by others to be extremely complex. If you are unsure or just don't know how to approach the problem, the following may be of some help.

On a technical but important note you should aim to have rigged all the lanterns required before you start the focus job. Yes, I know we all add the odd thing here and there, but in the main it's not a good idea to rig and focus as you go. For one thing, you will find it faster to rig all the lanterns first, but more critically if you try rigging multiple lanterns on the same bar/position you will inevitably knock and un-focus the lantern/s you had just finished with while trying to rig the next one to it. The beginner may regard this as a rather chicken and egg situation. "How do I know how many lanterns I need to make my coverage before I've finished focusing?" Read on.

First and most importantly, remember that you are working with multiple images/shapes which the human mind does not handle regularly. The shape of the light output from the lantern is conical, so your perception of what you can do with these shapes may need a little concentration - especially when you consider that the first thing you are going to do with these cone shapes is to tilt them on their sides so that they strike the floor or performer at an angle.

You need to picture the performance space as a three dimensional image. It may help if you sketch out the following, bearing in mind that for the purpose of this exercise we are dealing with an imaginary stage/area with an audience seated on one side (traditional end stage proscenium arch) with the requirement being to light the front stage acting area giving the audience a front lit view of the performers.

First picture a plan (overhead) view of the area. This will contain both the lantern, the starting point of your cone of light, the acting area to be covered being the end of your cone of light where it strikes the floor. Depending upon the angle of the lantern in relation to the floor this will vary from circular, being directly overhead, to elliptical where the lantern is at an angle.

Secondly, look at it as a front elevation view so your cone is in fact a triangle, the base being the stage floor and the pinnacle being the lantern. It's quite obvious that with a person standing in the middle of the cone of light, the centre of the base line will be lit from directly above. But what happens when

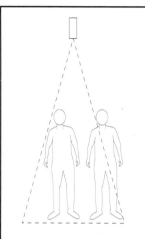

The front elevation shows the cone of light and how one performer is completely lit but the other is half in the dark.

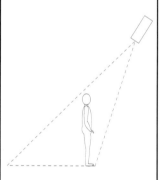

This actor is also perfectly lit, but if he steps backwards, his face will be in the dark. If he steps forwards, his face will still be lit, but his feet will not.

you move the person to a position at either extreme end of the base line, edge of the cone, or move the pinnacle position off to one side leaving the person still at the centre of the base line? The majority of the person (the important upper half) is unlit.

This is where your three-dimensional imaging comes into play. For a start, you can see one of the most basic rules (if there are any) of lighting design. "Don't light the floor and forget the actor." The part you need to concentrate on is between 1 and 2.5 metres above floor level at any given position.

So, is our first dimension plan view misleading? Not really. After all, you have to start somewhere and virtually all design plans are drawn up in plan view. But don't get carried away with the plan as a true representation of your design - remember the main reason for the plan existing is to show the equipment requirement to technicians who have to put it in place.

The second dimension (front elevation) is only half of the resolve to the cone coverage problem since it will provide a view of the lit area moving left and right. It's not until you combine the third dimension side elevation with the other two that you get a true representation of the coverage you have made.

Thirdly, picture the performer viewed from side stage left or right and just what happens to your cone of light, not only as it lights the performer but also what happens to it after it has passed the performer. At the point where it lights the performer the same effect and rules apply as described in the triangle/base line position. Where the light passes the performer it will cast a shadow, and normally this will simply fall onto the stage floor. But beware! If your lantern/s are positioned too low and have only a shallow angle of attack to the area to be lit, these shadows will cause a real problem, but more of this later.

So, with this imaging in mind, and with a requirement to 'light' across the front of a stage area, try to imagine how multiple lanterns/cones of light will combine together to provide a single coverage from one side of the stage to the other. The ability to achieve this is central to most good lighting design.

Of course, there is a little more to it than a theory of cone shapes sketched in three dimensions. For a start, this is one coverage from one angle/position. What happens further up stage from our imaginary area coverage? Well, more of the same. In fact, any number of times, building up a whole stage or area coverage as required. Just because we looked at a front stage area coverage don't think that this method has to be used in strips of light crossing the stage. When you have a stage area covered in this way the coverage will travel in all directions, in short you have to consider the three dimensional aspect of every part of the performance space. However, don't forget the two basic things which the lighting coverage is trying to achieve:

1. To light the performer and not necessarily the floor area.
2. To provide an even/seamless coverage of light both up and down and left and right over the given area.

Remember I said there was more to it? For a start, our imaginary coverage is in just one colour and unless you have the benefit of colour change units for each lantern, the whole thing needs to be duplicated over again to provide another colour coverage.

Yes, side lighting and back lighting are usually a requirement and are both extremely effective. But put them into priority order. Remember our three dimensional image of the lighted area. The audience will see the performer and usually expect to have the side facing them lit, so as said before, the lantern/light source will have to be somewhere between them and the performer. How would the same performer look if lit only by side and back light? Not the same, that's for sure. It may be very effective and it may even be exactly what you need it to look like but for most applications it just won't work.

Just imagine any end stage proscenium arch production lit in this way. It would look rather strange unless the performance work called for this style of lighting and of course there is just such a style dance where very little front light is used where traditionally quite a lot of top/direct overhead light and as much side lighting as can be accommodated. But let's not get too side tracked into specifics - the object of this book is to point the beginner in the direction of normality, with some basic ideas of what you should aim to achieve.

So, back to our focusing Fresnel. You can vary the focus (size) of the output so you focus the lantern onto the performance stage area - a simple enough task you would think. Usually it is, but just stop and think about what you are going to do. I offer the following few ground rules for consideration.

In focusing lanterns you will need a relatively dark if not totally blacked out workplace, because you can't see what you are actually doing with the lantern under any other light condition.

You will need two or three people, depending on the location of your lighting control desk. You may need an operator, you will need someone to do the focusing with hands on the equipment almost certainly at the top of a ladder or tower, and you, the lighting designer, who knows where you want the lanterns to 'focus', and you will of course be on the performance stage area directing operations.

You will need to have a quiet workplace. You cannot give instructions to the person at the top of the ladder and call circuit numbers to the lighting desk operator if the workplace is full of stage crew noisily building the set with Radio 1 in the background or the sound engineer trying out the sound system, or worst of all the piano tuner doing what piano tuners do. But if you have achieved a black out in the first place some of these noisy distractions will have gone away.

You need time, and for the beginner a lot more than you may think. Quite often the focusing session will take place very late at night or very early in the morning and no matter how much time you have or how experienced you are, you must get the focus right, because no matter how good the design concept, no matter how new and state of the art the equipment is, or how excellent the control desk operator is, if the lantern isn't pointing in the right place the rest won't help! If I could wish for one fact only to stay with you from your study of this book it would be this statement!

Back to our Fresnel lantern: area dark and quiet, personnel in place, off we go (at last) so what do you do? What do you say? First call for the dimmer channel controlling the lantern to be focused and if you are lucky the thing will actually come on. If it doesn't? Well that's another chapter; let's assume it works!

The act of focusing for the person on the ground is mostly a matter of personal preference. Some people will stand where they want the lantern to focus and look directly at the lantern and give instructions to the focuser. Some prefer to view the result from a distance, again giving instructions. Probably the most popular method is to stand in the position where the lantern is to be focused but with your back to the lantern so that you can see the light output on the floor with your shadow in it. One slight draw back to this is that you are now facing away from the person at the top of the ladder doing the hands-on work, so the instructions should be clear and loud - often accompanied by hand movements - telling the focuser left, right, up, down, larger, smaller and any actions required for barndoors or shutters.

Some people prefer to focus a lantern in white light, adding colour only when the final position has been set. Others prefer the colour to be applied from the start of the process. Whatever the choice, the most important thing is that at the end of the focus the lantern is locked tight in position, both pan and tilt. Of course, this action is made by the focuser, but the person on the ground should be satisfied that the locking off is compete. Don't be in too much of a hurry to speed your focuser onto the next lantern - remember it can be a difficult task at the top of a ladder in the semi-dark working with a hot lantern, especially at 2am when you are tired and have the prospect of several more hours of being shouted at from below. Indeed, if the focusing session is for a large rig of lanterns the hands on focusing should be rotated in shifts if at all possible.

Experience and practice will of course help, and it is often found that when a designer (on the ground giving instructions) works regularly with a focuser, an understanding will grow between the two, sometimes to the point where very little is said and with most actions happening almost automatically with a few hand gestures.

So you have focused a lantern and going back to our coverage we need to focus the next one. You will need to leave on the first lantern, possibly at a reduced light level, so that you can see where its coverage ends. It's then a relatively simple task to overlap the next lantern. Don't forget the cone effect and that at actor's head height the coverage will be smaller than it appears on the performance floor.

During this process you will find it useful to walk through the combined area of the two lanterns at the overlap position. Use your rig plan/clip board or simply the back of your hand to test and assess the meld between the lanterns making the coverage. This way, if you have any little holes in your coverage you can make adjustments.

So that's it. Simple really, and when the audience is enjoying the show they will have no conception of the hours of work that you and your team of technicians have put into it and at the end of the day very few people, if any, will compliment you on "how good the lighting was", because it won't have been noticed. But after all, the audience didn't come to see your lighting - they came to see the show. Now that doesn't worry you at all, does it? Of course, if the show needs lighting for 'effect' . . . then that's another story.

Of course, this scenario has assumed that you have not only the equipment but also the personnel and the time to operate in the way described. For lots of users you will at best have only one assistant and may find yourself doing all of the tasks alone. Yes, of course it's possible, but very time consuming.

The actions and theories involved in the focus process are common to most lanterns, although there is very little focusing in the use of floods, so the principles of the act of focusing can be applied to all of your lighting rig.

Within this section I have made reference to a rig plan. This is often a true scale drawing of the stage area, with the confines of the set drawn on it, the rig of lanterns also being scale representations of your equipment. If scale drawings are not available then a schematic representation can be used. This is fine for smaller events, venues and rigs but where you are working on a large project the scale imaging becomes very helpful and practically essential.

Your rig plan will contain not only the graphic information of set and lantern positions but should also give specific notation on at least three other major factors:

1. The circuit/dimmer number (represented by # or circled) associated with each lantern: #4
2. The approximate focus position: DSL (down stage left).
3. The colour, even if no colour, used in the lantern: 122 usually circled, no colour is normally shown as o/w (open white)

The circuit number #4 is normally placed behind the lantern, the colour normally placed within the representation of the lantern shape and the focus position normally placed in front of the lantern.

The rig plan will contain various other notes on the use of barndoors, iris, gobo and shutters, indeed anything that is relevant to the focus operation and depending upon the size of the rig involved it can become a rather complex document. I suggest that however simple your rig plan is, it's not likely to fit

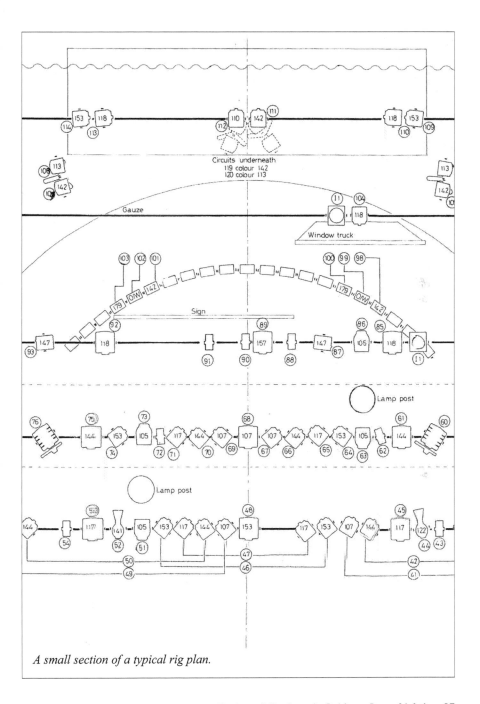

A small section of a typical rig plan.

on a sheet of A4!

If you have a tried and tested format for producing a rig plan then none of this will be new to you. If you are trying this for the first time you may benefit from the purchase of a lantern stencil, which will provide you with the various graphics you are likely to need in representing your lanterns.

Your rig plan has a number of functions – apart for checking your lantern coverage on a white surface! In the professional sense the designer will send the rig plan to the venue so that other people can put the equipment in place prior to the arrival of the designer (don't laugh too much, this really is how it happens in the professional theatre). The information, graphic, numeric and notation, really does have to get written down somewhere. It's not a good idea for the whole thing to stay only within the head of the designer. Finally, when you come to the plotting session (to follow) you will need to know circuit numbers etc, so the plan becomes quite a vital part of your lighting design.

Many people may perceive that "this lighting business" is over hyped and in any case modern technology (computer controlled moving lights) takes away most of the time consuming manual tasks. I could give you the full half hour of reasoned argument as to why this is just not so, suffice to say that cost and a whole load of other factors come into play.

Yes, the latest automated ranges of lanterns are becoming a major feature of performance lighting - but mainly as effect lighting. You can't really imagine scores or hundreds of moving lights being the only lighting sources for the average event. In a large scale West End production with mega budgets they are fine, but for the rest of us we are probably many years away, in technology/cost terms, from finding them the norm, so the fixed lantern and the critical focus will remain with us for many years to come.

2 A LITTLE MORE ADVANCED DESIGN PHILOSOPHY

So we have looked at what are the most common five lantern types - the flood, Fresnel, profile, prism convex and the Par, and each has a place in lighting the performance stage. We have also touched upon the first elements of design in the focus of a lighting coverage. However, design and focus are totally different elements of the lighting task, for the design is the job of turning your mind's eye vision into actual reality, whereas the focus is simply a mechanical function. But it cannot be stressed strongly enough that the whole lighting project can and will be won and lost in the focus.

Quite often you will find that there is very little 'conceived design' in lighting your production or event, for some very simple and basic reasons. For a start, a large proportion of people who take on the lighting job will not have access to limitless quantities of equipment and will be working with inadequate time - so my suggestions of a blanket area coverage may not be possible. This fact does not make the requirement any less desirable, just not possible. I suggest that you should at least try to regard this method as your aim. At least if you know the principles involved it may answer some questions as to why your lighting does not work, or could be better.

Let's take the focus of an area coverage a step further, and again we will assume we are working in a traditional proscenium arch space.

Divide the stage into three areas: left, centre and right. Remember we are dealing in stage technical terms, stage left being actor's left when looking into the auditorium. It matters very little, if at all, about the size of the stage because if you are dealing with a large stage you are likely to be working with 1.2 or 2kW lanterns which are working over quite a long throw (distance) whereas on a small stage you may be working with 500 or 650W lanterns working over a much shorter throw. The end result is that the light output in area coverage will be similar. You could of course divide the stage area into four or five areas but let's start with the regulation three.

Assume there is an over stage lighting bar directly upstage of the main house tabs and this is populated with 12 lanterns (Fresnels) spaced evenly within the proscenium opening. Starting at the stage left end of the bar focus the first lantern almost straight down, making a coverage of the downstage left area. Then focus the third lantern linking to the first, so covering downstage centre, and then the fifth linking to cover downstage right.

Now simply mirror this focus with lanterns seven (down left), nine (down centre) and eleven (down right). You now have the three stage areas lit from two positions (angles), and of course if you have achieved the coverage trick the whole of the down stage front area should be evenly lit from left to right. But we started off with 12 lanterns! What about the other six? OK. Now this is the really cleaver bit - but first you have to take on board just a little design concept.

Most stage lighting requirements will call for at least a two colour coverage: one in a warm colour, one in a cold colour. This simple statement could take at least a whole chapter to discuss and disseminate and probably will cause much comment along the lines of: "How boringly ordinary", "Not in this production", etc, etc. But remember the aims of my comments are to provide the beginner with a basic level of information and advice, and my advice is that "Most stage lighting requirements will call for at least a two colour coverage".

So, back to our other six lanterns. You probably won't be surprised that they should focus in exactly the same positions as the first six, but this now provides the opportunity for a second colour coverage.

Our first bar of 12 lanterns will of course be duplicated at a front-of-house position and at further overstage positions, continuing the coverage and extending it to cover as much of the stage area as required. It is quite normal for two or even three more bars of lanterns to be rigged and focused in this way.

For the purpose of our exercise we will use a pale straw or amber for one colour coverage and a pale steel blue or steel tint for the other. What this actually provides you with is a very powerful tool in the stage lighting armoury: the ability to light an area of the stage in either colour from either side.

Picture our proscenium stage complete with a box set (scenery forming the walls of a room starting at down stage left and running up stage, across stage and down to stage right). Let's assume there is a large French window in the stage left wall of the set, being the main source for 'natural daylight' into the room/set.

Now if we use as the strongest light source all of our lanterns positioned on stage left, i.e. lanterns 1-3-5 from our first overstage bar in the warm (pale straw or amber) coverage and complement this with lanterns 8-10-12 in the cold (pale steel blue/tint) coverage, the effect this will have on the performers

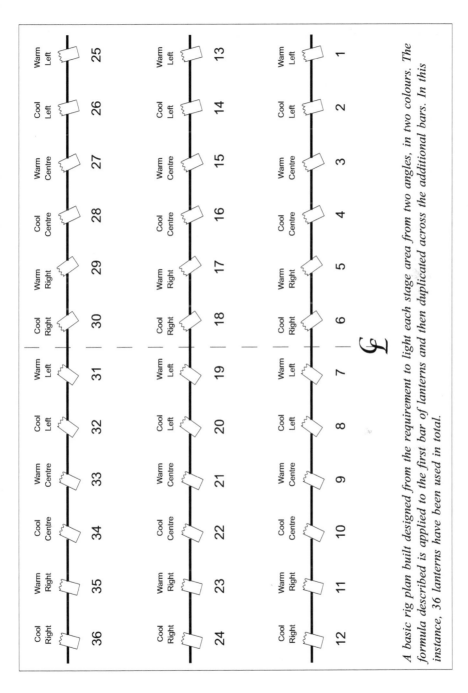

A basic rig plan built designed from the requirement to light each stage area from two angles, in two colours. The formula described is applied to the first bar of lanterns and then duplicated across the additional bars. In this instance, 36 lanterns have been used in total.

is that on one side (stage left where the light is supposed to be coming from) they will be lit with a warm colour representing and complementing the natural daylight, while on the other side the coverage will be colder, representing the darker and almost reflected light.

This is a very simple example and in real stage conditions there is quite a lot more to it than that, but I hope you get the idea of what is possible. Yes, you may argue that if you are trying to create reality it just doesn't look like that. Well may be, maybe not. Remember, you have to accentuate just a little for the stage and of course depending upon the nature and style of the production you will choose either a subtle or a vibrant range of colour.

This basic two colour multi-area coverage is of course only the start. I have not mentioned specifically the need for back light, side light, or in the case of the scenario of the box set, a large amount of light off stage focused through those French windows for effect.

I can hear you all moaning that my ideas and suggestions are way above your normal methods, because you just don't have the equipment and just how long will it take to focus! The whole idea is ridiculous, you may say.

Yes, I know that, but (and it's not a solution) when you go to see a production in a professional theatre that *does* have the facilities, the time and the budget, that's how it's done and albeit on a smaller scale how do you expect your production to contain similar results if you don't strive to do the same? As I said, it's not a solution, and for some it is perhaps a glimpse of Utopia.

Colour Choice

Now I am probably going to disappoint those of you who really needed help with the choice and use of colour, and here's why.

I have always regarded the choice of colour as a very personal thing - something akin to likes and dislikes of food. I am continually asked "what colour would you use" for a particular application and that very question is at the centre of my thoughts. What colour would "I" use - and of course the answer is likely to be something different, and of your own preference.

You will find that the modern day range of colour filters is vast and offers both a subtle and comprehensive choice. If I can give any help at all I will say that in my experience most lighting designers, me included, use quite a small pallet of colours, with probably less than 20 being 'favourites', and of these there is probably a hard core of ten or less.

There is one final thing very relevant to choice and use of colour. I can't quote you case study information, but I understand that more than 50% of the world population is colour blind to some degree, and therefore what *you* see may well be not be 'seen' in the same way by many others.

The most critical part of colour selection and use is being able to start from a blackout. It is sometimes difficult if you are working outdoors, but I'm sure you get the idea, because we can do lots of things with light and colour but it works best when we are in a controlled environment, and in a proper performance space a good 'blackout' is usually achievable. Those of you who are forced to operate in a multi-purpose (probably school) hall have my sympathy, but there's not a lot to be done to solve the problem, apart from persuading someone to invest in new blackout curtains!

3 DIMMERS AND CONTROLS

Dimmers

If you think about it, it's rather odd that having gone through the efforts of putting all your lanterns in the right place and having spent long hours getting the focus right, the first thing you want to do is limit the light output to less than the maximum potential!

Well, it's a little like driving your car. You rarely use the maximum available power, and the ability to use less than the maximum available is a very important factor in the end result of any lighting design.

The dimmer is simply a device which provides the user with a means of limiting the voltage/current reaching the lantern. For the purposes of basic explanation you will know that mains voltage in the UK is 230 volts, plus or minus a small percentage allowable by the electricity supply companies. Don't be confused if you see that existing older equipment, lamps etc, are rated at 240v which until recently was the standard UK mains voltage, it has been changed to bring all EEC countries into one common standard. Such equipment/ lamps will work quite happily, and you will notice very little if any change

Therefore, as the dimmer controls/limits the voltage to the lantern so the light output reduces. It is wise to note at this point, on a slightly technical matter, that as with most things in life you don't get something for nothing, and the price you pay for this 'control' is that heat (and sometimes noise) is generated by the dimmer. This is dealt with by various manufactures in a number of different ways, but inevitably the site of your dimmers will need to have good ventilation - sometimes requiring forced air extract. So, wherever possible dimmers are not placed in or near to the acting area. Of course, smaller portable dimmer systems are used in close proximity to the performing space, but do beware of the noise problem.

As with lanterns, dimmers vary in size/capacity and all are rated to control up to their maximum load, expressed as 'amperage'. So you need to know what load you are going to put on your dimmer - in other words the load of your lantern or lanterns. It's back to basic electrical practice and Ohms law. Don't be too concerned about getting technical. It really is very simple. We know two factors involved in this equation and we will use them to find the

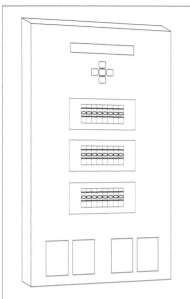

A wall-mounted hard-wired dimmer rack with three rows of fuses or circuit breakers - one for each electrical phase.

third and missing factor.

1. We know that mains voltage is 230 volts
2. We know that our lantern is rated at a specific Wattage (power rating of the lamp)
3. We need to know the amperage (load) and to calculate this we divide the Wattage by the voltage i.e. 1000 (Watts) divided by 230 (volts) = 4.35 (amps).

You will soon get used to the various amperage loads involved and associated with lanterns in common use.

Having made this calculation for your lantern/lanterns you can now safely connect them, either singly or in multiples, to your dimmer, in the knowledge that the total load will not exceed the capacity of the dimmer. As you will see, if you are working with a 10 amp dimmer you can safely load it with two 1000W lanterns (4.35 amps each, total 8.7 amps) but three would overload it (4.35 amps each total 13.05 amps).

A note of caution at this point! Just because the individual lantern(s) are

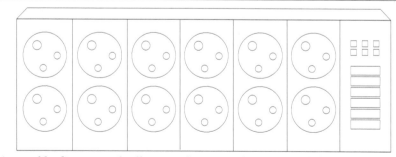

A portable dimmer pack alloes any lantern to be connected directly to any dimmer in the pack.

below the handling capacity of the dimmer(s), don't get carried away with the idea that that's the end of the matter; it's only half the story.

You must be sure that the overall capacity of the power supply feeding the dimmer(s) is large enough to cope with the total load involved i.e. if you are using a total of 12 x 1kW lanterns (total amperage of 52.2 amps) but the power supply to the dimmers is only 32 amps, as you can see you are likely to overload the supply – the result being a blown fuse or circuit breaker and of course no lights at all!

This situation is more of a problem in smaller temporary dimmer installations, since a larger fixed installation will have (should have) this type of calculation taken into account when the dimmer system was installed. Again, the overall calculation of the amperage required is vital, but of course things are never quite as simple as that.

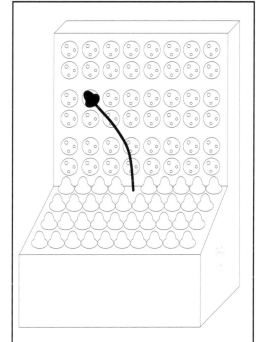

A patch panel allows any lantern in the rig to be connected to any permanently installed dimmer, a method often used where there is a limited number of dimmers, but far more socket outlets are needed around the rig for flexibility. The sockets in this diagram are connected to the dimmers and the plugs on flexible chords are wired back to socket outlets in the rig.

This situation leads us to apply what is called a 'diversity factor' - in other words we will assume that a quantity, less than the potential maximum, of lanterns will be used at any one time, and this is expressed as a percentage of between 30% and 50% below the maximum. The danger is that for the majority of your production this will be fine except for those odd occasions where a complete full up lighting state is used, may be accidentally, and results in a complete blackout when the main supply fuse blows!

The only sure way to avoid this problem is to make sure your power supply exceeds the maximum load demanded by your lanterns. Alternatively, don't use more lanterns than the supply can handle.

There are two main ways in which the lantern and the dimmer are connected. The first is where the lantern is plugged into a socket outlet which is in turn connected directly to the dimmer. This type of dimmer system is known as 'hard wired' and is rather limiting since you, the user, has no option as to which dimmer supplies which lantern or number of lanterns.

The second method of connection also relies upon plugging the lantern into a socket outlet, but before connection to the dimmer the wiring passes through a 'Patch Panel' (another plug and socket). It is the plug connectors on this panel which connect into the dimmers and gives this system the name 'patchable'.

Quite often the dimmer systems found in large venues will be hard wired and since there are more dimmers and outlets the seemingly limiting factor of one dimmer one lantern is not such a problem as it may at first appear. However, in a much smaller venue where there may be only 12 dimmers in total, to have them tied to just 12 specific lanterns/positions would probably make the lighting system very inflexible and difficult to use to any good effect.

Obviously there are some exceptions to these basic formats. For instance, you will regularly see large dimmer systems with a partial or even a total patch system built into it and you will find small dimmer systems that do work even though they are hard wired.

A note on electrical safety

At this point we need to delve into technical matters once again, and the realms of electrical installation regulations. I know you may not have been expecting this to be quite so technical, after all we have moved away from lighting a performance stage, but the next few facts are important for electrical safety, especially where the smaller venue is involved using a patchable dimmer system.

I said we all know that mains voltage in the UK is 230 volts, but are you aware that once out of your residential home and in a place of work such as almost any entertainment venue, albeit your local church hall, school stage or small theatre, the 230 volt supply will probably come from one of three different sources. These are called 'phases', each phase being a separate 230 volt supply. Other reference works will provide much better information on how and why our electrical system works in this way so I don't intend to spend much time trying to explain it in detail, but it may help you to understand just a few of the basics.

What is 3 phase power?

In the Alternating Current (AC) system, as the name implies the current alternates from the positive to the negative and back again in a continuous cycle - this being about 60 times per second, and it is called the frequency. The three electrical phases are simply three individual supplies which start at different times/positions of the frequency/cycle, each one having a 230 volt potential but out of time and synchronisation with each other.

Why 3 phase power?

The are two reasons for 3 phase power. First, the power requirements of a building may exceed, for example, a load requirement of 100 amps, and rather than simply making cables and fusing and distribution larger, it is easier to split the load into 3 parts and assign each part of the load its own 'Phase' of 230 volt power. Secondly, in a workplace environment there may well be equipment such as motors which actually need all three phases of electrical power in order to work.

Why does this effect my dimmer/stage lighting system?

Most electrical engineers, when faced with a large amperage load such as presented by a stage lighting system, will want to split and distribute the load over all three electrical phases, so that each phase has a balanced load in line with the rest of the building's electrical requirements. There is nothing wrong with this in theory, but in practice, especially within smaller venues and installations, it just does not work – for the following reason. Imagine your lanterns lighting the stage, let's say 30 at 1000W each, and the engineer has them split evenly, 10 to each of 3 patchable dimmer packs and each dimmer pack assigned to an individual (different) electrical power phase. In theory this is fine but what happens when you, just by coincidence, decide to use all 10 lanterns on one phase and none of the others? The result is total electrical phase imbalance, which is what the electrical engineer was trying to avoid in the first place.

As if this problem was not bad enough there is the added complication of electrical safety, for power from a 3 phase supply is a whole lot different than that from a single phase.

Many of us at some time or another have had an electric shock from a 230 volt supply and our usual reaction is to disconnect ourselves from it as fast as possible with a resolve not to do it again because it hurt and was unpleasant. Unfortunately, an electric shock from a multi phase power supply is not so straight forward, as the voltage involved may well affect the body's central nervous system to a point where despite your need to disconnect yourself from the cause of the shock you may be unable to do so. In other words, 3 phase power can be very dangerous in the wrong place.

It should be stated that all electric shocks, no matter what the voltage involved, has the potential to cause serious injury. It's simply that in most people's view, three phase power has the potential for greater danger if used incorrectly.

To help clarify this situation and make our lives safer, in the UK, The Health and Safety Executive have issued a guidance note (GS50 Electrical Safety in Places of Entertainment), part of which says that you should only supply a single phase power supply to any one lighting bar/boom. So that's all right then. We are nice and safe. Not quite, but we are getting there. Unfortunately, the electrical engineer who doesn't understand the vagaries of us funny theatre lighting people simply says: "The answer is to spread the load over all three phases". It would seem ideal simply to connect one dimmer pack to each electrical phase, but what happens when the user decides to patch three lanterns on adjacent outlets on one lighting bar into three dimmer channels which happen to be in different dimmer racks, thus being on different electrical phases? You have just done exactly what the GS50 guidance note says you should not do! And you could end up with a potentially dangerous electrical system.

In these days of personal accountability the onus falls upon the individual to both design and install a safe working electrical system and patchable systems using more than one phase of power are potentially unsafe. I know it's not much help, but even when you consult a supposed electrically qualified person, unless they have experience in the requirements of the performing arts they are likely to give you a safe system but one which is unusable in practical terms!

Yes, I know you can mark and label the system with the dos and don'ts about how you should use it and it may be that the person responsible is electrically competent and would never let it be used in such a way. However, none of that will actually prevent an accident and in these days of individual responsibility in the event of an accident in legal terms it will come down to the named individual who was responsible for both the design and the installation of such an unsafe system.

This all sounds very serious – and don't misunderstand me, it is! And I'm not advocating anything other than the use of *safe electrical systems*. The real point I am trying to make is that if you have a problem with your electrical supply, take advice from someone who is experienced both electrically and in the needs of the performing arts. If you achieve a safe electrical system without regard to what the system has to deliver in operating your lighting dimmers, you may well end up with a system that can fulfil only a small part of your needs.

One final point on the dimmer capacity. Remember I said earlier that dimmers are rated to control up to their maximum stated capacity and in this they operate providing a smooth dimmer curve. Well the ability of the dimmer to control at the low end of the power handling scale is sometimes also important, and is not often specified by the manufacturers unless you get into the very technical details of the dimmer.

Of course, for the vast majority of uses you will be concerned with lanterns and loads which approach the capacity of the dimmer, but occasionally you will need to control or dim a very small load, such as a single table lamp or a set of fairy lights. In theses cases, because the load is only a few Watts you may find that the dimmer operates almost like a switch with hardly any dimming curve at all. Again, this may not be a problem, particularly if you are just switching things on/off.

Should you need this small load to fade at the same rate as the remaining lighting (have the same dimming curve) you may need to 'load' the dimmer channel with another load/lantern. This can be positioned off stage away from the acting area where its light output is of no consequence to the performance lighting, and this additional 'load' will then make the visible small load fade at the same rate as the rest of the lighting/dimmers. However, most modern digital dimmers should be able to handle loads as low as 40W or even 15W in the case of a quality dimmer, so the practice of dummy loads is becoming a thing of the past.

But let's not spend any more time worrying about the technical side of dimmers and power supplies. You have your lanterns plugged in and are ready to start. Well not quite – for the dimmer is only the engine of the system, and to make it work you need a steering wheel: the control desk.

Control Systems

For the purpose of at least appearing to be up to date and using modern technology, I do not intend to dwell on the old wire wound resistance dimmer boards. In the interests of your sanity, and any hope of providing the modern standards required in performance lighting.

if any of you are still using these things you should stop immediately! We are dealing here with electronic dimmers and control desks.

Large or small, inexpensive or top of the range, the control desk will be either manual or manual + memory or memory. Let's start with the basic manual control desk.

This will usually be a 2 preset desk, a preset being a bank of faders with individual connection and control of each individual dimmer. So, 18 dimmer channels will need an 18 channel control desk, but why the preset? So that you can *pre-set* the next lighting state and each 'preset' will normally have a master fader associated with it.

Quite often on a 2 preset desk one of the master faders will be inverted so that when both master faders are placed together the action of moving them up and down will increase one and decrease the other. The modern preset control desk will also contain a timing device and often another fader so that when set to a required time and the master faders moved, the fade/change from one preset to the other takes place in the time selected.

The manual + memory control desk will have all the attributes of the manual desk plus the ability to record and play back lighting states programmed by the user. These desks are a small dedicated computer and many of them will have simple effects and chase programs built in.

Example of a 12 channel two-preset manual desk. The controls may include flash buttons, preset masters, manual crossfade, timed crossfade, grand master fader and blackout switch.

The memory control desk may have limited ability for the user to have a fader hands on control of every dimmer channel but will have extensive computer control power to call up, adjust, memorise, modify, combine and replay limitless lighting states.

It is worth noting that serious computer buffs have now given up the struggle to try to convince the theatre lighting world that a QWERTY keyboard can control lighting for the entertainment industry, and that all serious control desks are now based upon a dedicated control panel. True, the computing power behind the panel is now becoming very similar to that of the average microchip based computer and it's also true that the larger systems often use QWERTY keyboards for some functions - but no matter which manufacturer you chose you will be operating a control desk which is used for no other purpose than to control lighting for entertainment.

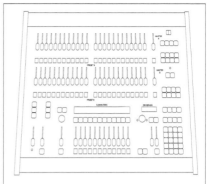

A manual+memory control system will have individual channel faders and manual crossfade and the lighting states can be stored in internal solid state memory or portable memory cards or disks. The system may also include submasters, an effects generator, a keypad for memory and/or channel selection, an optional visual display unit, etc. A system like this has the capability of controlling up to 512 channels although it is most likely to be used for control of 60-120 channels.

Most manual and manual + memory controls work by providing the dimmer with a low voltage control signal. These desks are called analogue control desks and they need one dedicated wired connection for each dimmer used plus a reference or control voltage and an earth reference, so our 18 dimmer channel system with manual control will require 20 individual wires to connect it together. This wiring, known as control wiring, is made in very light duty cable of a similar grade to that used in telephone connections. It is often grouped together in multiples of eight (6 dimmer channels 1 control voltage line and 1 earth reference line), all combined in a multipole connector with 8 pins. This format is now regarded as standard by most major manufacturers, however some older systems may use different types and styles of connector.

The more modern memory control systems operate in a different way for they have a digital output. Just like the computer language which they use to operate, the digital output is a series of electronic pulses or on/off commands which are continuously updated and run at extremely high speed. All of this digital information passes down one twin + screen signal cable and because of the speed at which it runs masses of data can be transmitted down the same signal line at the same time. This is known as a multiplex signal.

However, when the signal reaches the dimmers, unless they are very modern digital dimmers, it will need to be transformed into an analogue (voltage) format so that the dimmers can react to it. This is done with a digital to analogue converter known as a de-multiplex, or demux unit. For large dimmer systems you will immediately see the benefit of only needing one twin screen signal cable rather than tens or even hundreds of individual wires, and we are now starting to see quite small systems (12 dimmer channels) being supplied with this multiplex signal output.

The multiplex signal used in this form of control can appear in many different forms known as protocols, the most widely used being DMX512 which the theatre/performance industry has adopted more or less as its standard. You will find that the multiplex/DMX signal is now being used to control many peripheral items of equipment such as colour scroll changers, dimming shutters, moving lights and quite a few other items of equipment which may not be lighting at all, such as smoke machines, haze generators, indeed any piece of electrical equipment which needs external remote operation.

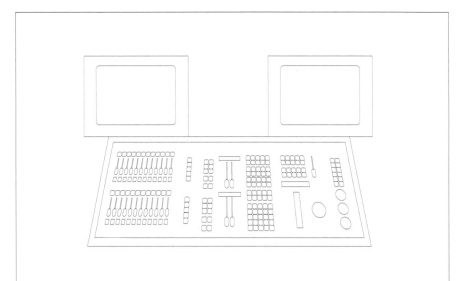

Example of a medium specification memory control system. Facilities include a keypad for channel and memory selection, banks of submasters, sophisticated automatic crossfaders, effects generators, support for up to 4 video monitors and possibly integrated controls for moving lights. This system can typically control up to 2048 channels.

But back to lighting control. Apart from their memory functions and digital output the larger memory control desks differ from the manual desks in two other major ways. First, and because they are commonly used to control upwards of 100 dimmer channels, they will have a display monitor (possibly two or more) for the user to see and read the status of the dimmer channel or memory playback in use. Second, all of the access to the dimmers and play backs is made on a numeric key pad.

These larger style desks often have a number of individual faders, known as submasters, and these can be programmed to control either individual dimmer channels, or more commonly groups of dimmer channels, in the form of memorised lighting states.

4
RIGGING

You will have spotted by now that that the technical side of theatre has a language all of its own. We talk about lanterns (not spots), lamps (never bulbs), and now 'rigging'. My dictionary has five definitions of rig or rigging and none involve theatre/performance use. However, one definition does talk about doing things in haste, or a makeshift manner, and that could well be right!

In many performance-related places things are often done in great haste, and in most cases look as if they have involved both Mr Heath and Mr Robinson. The trouble is that quite often the 'things' technical theatre people do are still in place several years later!

The business of rigging covers a wide range of things and quite a few of them involve getting them up in the air. So, in addition to your newly-found talents as a lighting designer and/or electrician, you also need to be a structural engineer! Perhaps not. In most theatre/performance spaces any such qualification would probably stop the whole show since anyone with this knowledge would never let us theatre technical types get away with what we do in the name of art. But all this does have a very serious side.

In most cases the need to hang, suspend, fly or fix your equipment above the performance space or auditorium, is usually one of the last things given careful consideration and planning. More often its a case of "well it's only going to be there for a few days", and, of course, in 99% of cases your production will run without any problems. Unfortunately, and probably due to rather bad 'accepted practice' and old ad-hoc methods, things do sometimes go wrong.

Let's take a look at a typical scenario. When the person who fixed a lighting bar in place in the village hall did the job in 1966, providing even then, inadequate suspensions for half a dozen Pattern 23s, he would have had no idea that some enterprising lighting designer would decide to hang three effects projectors (Pattern 252 plus effects disc) on the same lighting bar almost 30 years later - with disastrous results.

1966 = Patt 23 weight approx. 4.5kgs x 6 = less than 30kgs   as against

1996 = Patt 252 plus effects disc and lens weighing approximately 30kgs x 3, total 90kgs

plus those 6 x Patt 23 weighing approximately 4.5kgs x 6 = less than 30gks

= total 120kgs minimum.

The result is that the bar suspensions fail, and the whole lot falls onto the audience, causing serious injuries to several people who require hospital treatment. The performance is lost, and there are subsequent claims for personal injury, damage to property (both the village hall and the suppliers of the additional lighting equipment) - not to mention the bad publicity.

And possibly worse still, don't forget that as a consequence of such an accidental happening, there would be an investigation, and more than likely a prosecution which might well be against several parties: the village hall (manager or person responsible), the performing company and probably the individual who rigged the equipment. You can also imagine the number of claims and counter claims that would ensue. In short, the whole thing ends in a complete nightmare - all because someone rigged equipment without due regard to all the circumstances.

Now I am not suggesting that every time you want to move, add or rig any additional equipment you have got to stop and consider my doomsday scenario. If that were the case, nothing in performance theatre would ever get done. But I *do* suggest that when rigging equipment, whether lighting or scenery, props or sound, you pause to consider the following points:

1. Despite (even in-spite) of previous excepted practice can you be sure it is safe?

2. It is often the structure and not the means of rigging that can be the failure point.

3. If possible, have the work done by someone with previous knowledge and experience.

There are two important facts to note. Firstly, it is not a defence to claim ignorance of regulations or the use of previously excepted practice. Secondly, much Health & Safety legislation puts the onus onto specific individuals, not an XYZ theatre company limited, and in doing so uses such phrases as *"shall have taken all reasonable precautions to prevent danger"*, the precise meaning of which is open to a wide range of interpretation.

In practice you will find that in almost every place of work (apart from your home and the highway, that means almost everywhere else), it is now common to find a person responsible for matters of Health & Safety. But don't get carried away with the idea that this person can solve all your problems or give you answers or guidance on a specific matter. In the main they can't. Indeed, much emphasis in Health & Safety matters is put upon the individual to self-assess the risk factors involved in what they are doing, and if a situation or a

Suspension designed and built in previous decades is unlikely to be suitable for heavier modern loads and equipment.

problem occurs, to report and seek guidance from someone in a more senior position and with more experience.

None of this helps you very much when you are running out of time and desperately trying to get your production in place. If there is one thing that can help it is better forward planning. However, the things which cause most problems tend to be those which crop up at the last minute or were unforeseen.

None the less, the act of rigging things in, around or above a performance space will continue, and what gives most cause for concern are objects and equipment which have to be suspended or 'flown', and there are some obvious points which will help.

If suspending an object (lighting bar) to be either fixed or moveable, check its weight, and if necessary, calculate the total load involved (the bar, its fixings/suspensions and the lanterns to be suspended from it). This will than be divided by the number of suspension points. It should be assumed that the total load involved will be "evenly distributed" over the length of the bar, thus evenly as a weight or "point" load at every suspension point suspending the bar. You should be confident that your structure and suspensions can support the loads proposed.

Ask if the suspensions have any SWL (safe working load) details (winch sets often do, as do load tested suspension points). If not, then take advice as to the load bearing capability of the suspension in use.

When providing suspensions, for example for a lighting bar, it is generally accepted that a minimum of three suspension points are used, so that in the event of one point failing the two remaining points should hold the bar more or less in the horizontal position. If only two suspensions are used, the failure of one will cause the bar to fall with a pendulum action, with the obvious hazards to anyone below. Obviously the longer the bar, the more suspension points will be required, please don't misunderstand my example about three suspensions per bar, if you are unsure how many suspensions to provide, you will need to seek advice.

Never assume that because something has been rigged previously that the structure and means of suspension are adequate or in order. Always check first.

There are any number of important considerations to be taken into account, and some of the answers will not be easy to find. For instance, who is going to know if the roof structure in your village hall will support an additional 75kgs of lighting equipment?

There will come a point (quite early in your rigging planning) when you will have to estimate to the best knowledge available, just what is safe and acceptable and what is not. Having gone through the exercise, can you argue that your interpretation of "shall have taken all reasonable precautions to prevent danger" is satisfactory?

One last point about rigging. Really, it's a step further than rigging, but it's a point which often gets overlooked or even completely forgotten. This is your means of access to equipment at high level - in other words the use of ladders or other equipment used to get you up in the air.

Many who never get involved with the technical side of theatre, and I have come across quite a few intelligent professional people who fall into this category, simply don't realise that when you have got your equipment up in the air, you have to go up to adjust, maintain or focus it! Surely, they say, you just wind the lighting bar down to the floor, load your lanterns, set their positions, and then wind the lighting bar up again. If only it were that simple! Of course, you could adopt this course of action, but as those who use this type of equipment regularly will tell you, it's just not a practical way of doing things.

The only sure way to achieve the end result you require is to climb up and get your hands on the equipment when it's in place at high level. In any case, quite a lot of things get rigged in places which do not have the luxury of any raise and lower action.

So the ladders come out from under the stage or wherever they are kept - and what a motley collection of gravity defying devices I have seen over the years. Some do well to stand upright by themselves without any thought of some brave soul climbing up them. The point is that the one action which is guaranteed to provide more risk than almost all the other technical things you do put together is to get you 15 or 20 feet off the ground, up some rickety old set of steps.

Remember that some stage areas are raked (sloping from back to front) and that despite knowing that it's not a good idea, you will be going up the ladder without anyone holding on to the bottom of it and probably to a height which it and thus you were never designed to reach. If you find yourself in this sort of situation, you should really be making a stand on the dangers involved and get someone to provide a safe and suitable means of access.

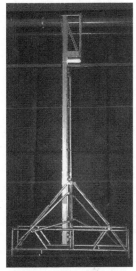

Proper access equipment should be used when working at height.

Need I say more?

By the way, you may find that in certain circumstances you will be discouraged or even not permitted to do the climbing job, for there are any number of local authority and even company regulations that state who may climb up what type of device, and to what height. So, if in any doubt, ask first.

5 THE LIGHTING TECHNICAL

Plotting

Remember what I said about never having enough time and just how long the focusing session can take? Well, here's another time-consuming job. I know that many people will regard this as a luxury and that for others the only form of plotting or lighting technical will be within a rehearsal – possibly even the final dress rehearsal!

If you find yourself in this sort of position you really should emphasise to your producer/director that you need a proper allocation of time for technical matters. Of course, this conversation will have taken place weeks or even months beforehand and a comprehensive technical schedule will have been agreed and all parties made aware of the times and requirements (another utopian dream). Seriously, the technical schedule is not that difficult to plan. Simply work backwards from the first night/performance, filling in the known requirements: final dress, first dress, full run + technical, full run - technical, technical run, plotting, focusing. Of course you can mix and amend any of this selection to suit whatever is normal for your event. The whole point is to create a sufficient amount of 'technical' time.

The job of plotting the lighting or the technical lighting session is a combination of at least two main objectives: those of the lighting designer and those of the director. One should have a clear idea of what a particular scene or set has got to look like and also the ability to create it. Problems will occur if either party has differing views or an inability to deliver – or even a different interpretation of what the end product is to be.

In many ways this aspect of technical matters comes first in the whole process, and is usually planned well in advance of any of the hands-on jobs. The director, probably the set and costume designers and you, the lighting designer, will hopefully have agreed the style and overall requirements of the show, so that when you sit down at the plotting session what you present is broadly in line with what everyone wants.

Of course, as you are the lighting designer the onus is usually on you to deliver a lighting performance, just like any performer on stage, and within this requirement there are two routes to take. Firstly, you can listen to the requirements of the director and take specific instructions, even down to what colours to use and at what position to rig and focus lanterns.

Secondly, in conversation with the director you can gauge the requirements and come up with your interpretation of the lighting design.

The second option is more normal, but remember the bit about agreeing the style and overall requirements of a production. Don't forget that people will see (literally) things in a different light. What may seem perfectly acceptable to you as representing a bright moonlit night may look nothing like that to others. Familiarity with your equipment will help with what you need to produce, as will your affinity with the director.

Plotting of the lighting states, as with the focusing session, is very difficult to do this while others are working within the performance area. For one thing, you will need to achieve a blackout condition again. Most plotting/lighting sessions will take place with you, the designer and director front and centre in the auditorium at what is known as the production desk, and this needs to be large enough to accommodate your lighting rig plan, various other paperwork, a communications talk-back system and a desk light – all being built so that it does not collapse into the seating as soon as you put your pen to work!

In today's technological age the lighting control desk, being a small computer, will often find its way onto the production desk, which will help matters no end since the operator will be at your side instead of in a control room position.

However, you may be working with older and much more basic equipment such as a preset control desk and this will probably not be at the production desk position. In either case your responsibility as the lighting designer is to instruct the control operator first what dimmer channels are needed and at what level, to create the desired lighting state, and second exactly how these states come together to achieve the changes required.

There is quite a subtle difference in professional theatre between the lighting designer and the lighting operator. Often both can and do change jobs, although not usually within a single production. The point is that both will usually have the ability to do the other's job, and this can sometimes cause stressful situations. It's a little like the actors knowing better than the director, but someone has to have the final say and it's usually the designer. Depending upon your circumstances it may of course be that you are actually doing both jobs, and this is not an uncommon situation. You will therefore have to balance the needs of the design requirements against the ability/skill of the control operator. It's an interesting problem, but console yourself in the knowledge that you can take yourself to the pub later for half the cost and definitely enjoy the company.

At this point you will be creating lighting states which, if you are lucky, the director will like, and you or your control operator will be either writing down (for preset control desks) or simply recording (for memory control desks) the information.

There is normally one other person at the production desk, the stage manager or deputy stage manager. This person is going to call or cue the whole show, and while you are busy getting the lighting states sorted out the stage manager will be taking down the relevant information into the prompt book so that each lighting change can be given as a cue to the control operator.

There are two important points to note. I know that many amateur companies and lots of others who simply don't know any better will say that "our lighting people take all their cues themselves from reading their own copy of the script". Well, not in my world they don't. It's just not possible to read text, watch the stage and work the control desk all at the same time with any degree of success, even in a slow moving two handed play, let alone a fast moving musical. No, it all comes down to the stage manager, for it's this person's job to bring together all the technical departments so that they are given all the information they need to do the relevant technical job at the right time.

The second critical point, which also involves the stage manager, is the language used - not the profanities, but the actual words and their order when used in talking to the technical departments. Most technical theatre in performance uses a communications system whereby each operator and the stage manager wears a headset (earphones) with a microphone so that everybody can give and receive information. Those using such a system for the first time should be (must be!) discouraged from idle chatter. The 'comms' network is not in place to discuss the football results, organise the after show party or any topic other than the technical job in hand. And it's at this point that the order of words and the language used is vitally important.

Stage Manager "Stand By Electric's (LX) cue 47"
Lighting Control "LX cue 47 standing by"

The stage manager will have agreed the length of the stand by period beforehand with all technical operators.

Stage Manager "LX cue 47 GO"
Lighting Control will action the cue on the command word GO

It all looks and sounds very simple – and it is – but just put yourself in the position of the stage manager who has to give technical cues to all departments: lighting, sound, off stage effects, flys, followspots and any number of others as well as, in addition to calling the acting company from the dressing rooms, keeping times of the performance, and following the script or score. And he could be prompting the acting company if needed. If you have a good stage manager do all you can to keep him or her, for this person will help make your show a success. A bad one who panics at the slightest hint of a problem, however, can ruin your technical efforts and should be encouraged to find an alternative way of spending their evening.

The point about language and order of words is that the command word GO must be the last word given, so that the control operator, already on standby, is given all of the information again just prior to the action.

LX lets the operator know this is for them and no other technical department. Cue 47 gives again the precise nature of the cue to be performed, GO being the exact moment that the change is made or started. Don't forget that the technical department put on standby should acknowledge this to the stage manager as follows: "LX standing by cue 47".

But why is this so relevant? Because the system of cueing must be geared to the most needful situation, such as when a lighting cue, with instant effect, must be performed at a precise moment in the action, for instance when an actor switches on a table lamp or light switch. Yes, I know that in the main this type of cue is taken as a visual cue by the lighting operator, but there will come a time when the operator must rely on the stage manager to give the cue in exactly the right place, so the method of giving the cue must be correct and the same every time.

So while you are noting the information which is the lighting state, your stage manager and the director will be agreeing and noting down exactly where the cue is given in the action/text.

Now back to our lighting plotting session. For those of you with experience of this procedure who probably have a perfectly good working system, none of this is particularly revealing. For others who are looking forward to their first attempt at this task I offer a few helpful dos and don'ts.

If you are using a memory lighting control desk, spend a few minutes making up some lighting states, 6 or 10 should be enough and they can be recorded into some high memory numbers. Regard these as building blocks - they can be used as they are or of course mixed and combined to make new states for re-recording. A memory lighting desk that has submasters is particularly useful for this type of forward planning.

Again, for those using a memory control, don't get carried away with using memory numbers in association with cue numbers. The modern memory control may well have the ability to insert what are called point cues e.g. cue 1, cue 2, cue 2.1, cue 2.2, cue 3, etc, etc but older systems will not have this feature and very soon your plotting of the show will have the cue numbers out of sync with the memory numbers. Remember, it is really only the lighting control operator who needs to know which cue number is associated with which memory. The stage manager is only interested in giving the lighting cue and has too much else going on to be concerned with which memory number is used.

Don't be afraid to re-use lighting states that you have used before. Of course, on a memory control desk this is simply a process of re-recording a memory / cue with a new number.

All memory controls will have a facility to selectively or automatically sequence your lighting states (memories). This feature gives the control operator the opportunity of an easy life, for starting with the first recorded memory it is feasible to work through the whole show by just pressing the go button on cue. Don't be afraid to make use of this feature, but don't be surprised when you find that the operation theory is not quite as simple in practice.

Try to get away from the stereotype copy of lighting changes and effects called for in the script or libretto. If the action calls for the leading lady to enter and turn on a desk light as an integral part of the action, it follows that you will need to plot a lighting cue, but don't think that you have to slavishly follow the instructions to the letter. Remember, especially with older productions, that the lighting plot was constructed using equipment of the day and you should be able to achieve better results with your modern equipment.

Lighting plotting sessions will also need at least one other person present, someone to walk the stage so that when you have created your lighting state, you can see and check that all the relevant areas are covered. Yes I know that you will have checked the coverage during the focus process, so you should be confident that there are no black holes, but your director may not be so confident and anyway it's good to check again just in case the stage crew may have re-arranged your focus when they put that last little masking border in place!

The lighting plotting session can sometimes drag on, so it's not a good idea to schedule it prior to a specific event such as a rehearsal; it is far better if it can start at a time with no specific end deadline.

When the session has finished, probably after a good night's sleep, it's quite normal that the control operator spends some time in editing, re-recording and generally tidying up the lighting states. This will not usually change the specific lighting states but just make them more useable.

For those operating a manual control system this time will normally be spent in re-writing cue sheets and checking that there is enough time to achieve the presets required between cues.

I apologise if this section seems biased towards the modern standards (memory control desks) when there are still many hundreds indeed thousands of you out there using the good old fashioned preset controls. However, the price of technology is falling year after year and it is now common to find memory controls in use in schools, colleges and many other places where a few years ago people were using wire wound resistance dimmers.

Indeed, I know of one venue where within the last few years they have gone from water dimmers (yes, real acid pot/water dimmers) to state-of-the-art electronic dimmers with on-board memory back up, in one step. Times and technology are changing fast!

6 CONCLUSION – DESIGN

For those of you who thought, from the title of this book, that you would be given some pointers towards stage lighting and design, you may well have been surprised at the many other aspects of technical theatre which have also been raised, such as electrical safety, various parts of Heath & Safety legislation, and the role of others – such as the director and stage manager – in your lighting works.

If you think about it, it's not that strange that when you involve a group of people in putting together any sort of event, that they all interact with each other to achieve the end result. The point is that what is expected of you from being in charge of the lighting is that you must not only deliver, but must do so in sympathy and in relationship to the other people and design elements involved.

If we assume that you are familiar with what the equipment will do and how and where to rig and use it, the design element of the job is all important, and this usually has to take input from several people, first the director and second the designer (set and costume).

Some of you will find yourselves working with a very small team of people with some departmental roles being combined, so the formal business of agreeing the style method and execution will be easy.

Many will have previous experience and use a regular venue with systems and tried and tested methods. If it works for you - and it's safe - with a good end product, then keep it up.

For those with limited experience, the design element may at first seem an almost intangible exercise. What is there to design? Remember my comments about achieving a lighting coverage in two colours? Surely there must be more to it than that? Of course there is, but for those of you working with limited time, budgets and resources perhaps the most important of all the golden rules it the one that says: "Get the simple basic area lighting done to a good standard and don't get carried away with all the fancy effects".

Make sure that your audience can see the performers in the way you and your director intend them to be seen. Then, if you have time, budget and resource you can indulge yourself with all the little extra touches, which can make all the difference to the lighting.

So why didn't I mention the business of liaison with directors and other designers at the start, since you might regard this as the first step in the whole process? Well, there is little point in getting involved in design principals if you are unsure about what a prism convex lantern will do for you, or suggesting a rig of 10kW of back light when the whole power supply available will only support 15kW in total.

You need to have some basic understanding of the equipment, what it will do and how it works together, before you can have any meaningful input to the design.

So, if you have got this far, you should feel a little more confident about the design, because you will be aware that Flood lanterns on the number 1 bar over stage and the Fresnel lanterns in the FOH positions, are not really best placed to do the job and you should perhaps have picked up some ideas about the quantity of lanterns and other equipment needed to bring about the lighting you intend to create.

But I didn't say what the design was. I suppose everyone will regard it as something slightly different, but for me it's simply a process of putting my mind's eye image of light (the output from a lantern) or multiple lights, down on paper and then being able to turn this theory from the paper, into the actual equipment and then through the focus and plotting to the performance, where if I am lucky it will actually look like my mind's eye image.

Did I use the word simply? Don't forget all the variables, just a few of which are: positions/angles, intensity, colour (choice) and also include a large element of other people's perceptions.

Early in the planning stage (very early) you should be able to gauge which of the two routes you will take to form opinions over the design, i.e. is it your design or are you under instructions? You can of course take several views on either route. You may know the play, musical or whatever and base your intentions upon making your lighting better than the last time your saw it. You may not know it at all and you may feel that you have to sit through the rehearsals to find out just what is required.

Your director, sometimes even the set designer, may have very specific ideas about the lighting. In this case you may regard yourself as little more than a rigger rather than a designer.

Whichever design path you follow, you will probably experience the complete range of emotions about what you produce. Sometimes you may feel totally inadequate and that what you have provided is less than expected: at other times you may surprise yourself with the results.

There is a reverse law of diminishing returns which is not surprising when you think about it. This is, the more equipment you use to light the production the more things that you never planned appear as if by magic before your eyes. But don't run away with the idea that just to saturate a production with masses of equipment and light will make it all right. Some of the most effective lighting I have seen and been responsible for was achieved with a minimum amount of equipment.

For a large proportion of you all this talk about directors, set and costume designers, not to mention the technical crew, is of course pie in the sky. Your group just doesn't operate with all these people involved, and the idea of design doesn't start with what lanterns to use in which position, but rather, shall I change the focus or colour of anything from the last production! If that really is the case, then at least having read this far you must have a better idea of your future goals!

I hope that these few pages have given you some helpful hints or at least have removed some of the mystery and technical jargon involved with lighting for the performance stage - or perhaps given a few of you a good laugh at just how wildly out of step I am with what *your* norm is.

But please remember, as I said at the beginning, this isn't a story or a complete work. It is only about the *'Basics'* - where I have tried to keep in touch with what I regard as some of the more essential elements of stage lighting.

GLOSSARY

This list is by no means comprehensive. It is intended only to give a quick reference to those words and phrases which cause most confusion to the beginner.

#:   Used to denote the dimmer circuit number (#4) on a rig plan.

Asymmetric: or off set reflector. This gives a light intensity bias to the output of the light, normally found in modern Floodlights (see page 14).

Axial: Orientation of the filament within the modern range of Tungsten Halogen lamps, where the filament lies in the same horizontal as the lens tube, i.e. at right angles to the reflector (see page 24).

Barndoor: Attacment that slots onto the front of non-profile lanterns to contain spill and softly shape the beam (see page 21).

Batten: Older style of Floodlight unit, suspended above the stage area, mainly used to light the cyclorama or back cloth.

Blackout: Lighting condition from which to start a lighting / plotting session, or, to achieve a good "blackout" within the performance area, or, to go to a Blackout.

Call: To Call or Cue the technical departments. Usually a member of the Stage Management team will be responsible for this function.

Cap: The Cap / connection end of the lamp, sometimes pins, sometimes a bayonet type fitting (see page 24).

Carrier: Lens Carrier, the mechanical holder for one or more lenses, within the lens tube of a profile lantern, providing the ability to move the lens backwards and forwards.

Colour Filter: A thin acetate film, which will withstand the high temperatures generated by the modern range of lamps, available in a wide selection of colours (see page 42).

Colour Magazine:	Usually associated with Followspots, providing a mechanical means of placing colour into the beam of light.
Coms:	abbreviation for Communications system, a low power amplification system providing personal headset equipment, sometimes called 'talkback' worn and used by all members of the technical team, to send and receive instructions (cueing)
Coverage:	The usually seamless coverage of lighting over a given area, also sometimes called a 'wash' (see pages 39-42).
CSI:	Compact Source Iodide: type of discharge lamp often used in modern followspots (see page 26).
Cue:	A lighting state, a cue given by the stage manager, to action a lighting change.
Cyclorama:	Usually a plain cloth at the back of the stage.
DeMultiplex:	Digital control signal, also known as DeMux and DMX used as the control protocol linking control desk and dimmers, and other technical equipment (see page 54).
Dimmer:	Electronic device to limit the flow of electrical current, used in multiples, modern dimmers being controlled by DeMultiplex signal (see page 45).
Discharge Lamps:	An enclosed arc light source, of various types, used in followspots and larger TV specification lanterns (see page 26).
DMX:	See DeMultiplex above.
Flat Field:	The ability to distribute the light output (in a Profile lantern) over the whole of the image, specially important when using Gobos.
Floodlight:	Any lantern having an open front, i.e. no lens (see page 13).
Floor Can:	Parcan lantern designed to be used from a floor position, often having an integral stand (see page 20).
Focus:	The act of positioning a lantern following the rigging process, critical in the overall lighting job (see page 30).
FOH:	acronym: Front Of House, being any public area, usually referring to the auditorium seating area.

Followspot:	High output profile type lantern, with handles and other user operating devices (see page 17).
Footlights:	Old, now mostly redundant form of Floodlight, found at the front floor position of a proscenium arch stage. Also known as 'floats'.
Fresnel:	One of the five main categories of lanterns (see page 14).
Gate:	Opening in the top of the lens tube of a profile lantern, behind the lenses, into which accessories such as Gobos or Iris Diaphragm may be inserted (see page 17).
Gobo:	Metal plate etched with a pattern / image, used within a Profile lantern to project the image, used within a Gobo Holder – may also be used in a Gobo Rotator (see page 21/22).
Ground Row:	Floodlight unit, mainly used to light the cyclorama or back cloth being floor mounted (see page 14).
HMI:	Halide Metal Iodide type of discharge lamp often used in Followspots and moving lights (see page 26).
Hook Clamp:	Sometimes called a 'G' clamp, used as the suspension link between the lantern and the lighting bar (see page 22).
Iris Diaphragm:	Used within a Profile lantern, to restrict the aperture / light output of the lantern (see pages 21-22).
Lamp House:	Rear section of the lantern, containing the lamp and reflector.
Lens Tube:	Front section of a Profile lantern, containing one or more lenses.
Light Curtain:	A line of low voltage narrow angle output lamps, contained in one housing, normally used in multiples, producing a narrow strip of high intensity light.
Memory Control:	Lighting control desk having the ability to memorise multiple lighting states (see page 53).

| **Moving Lights:** | These fall: into two types, moving head and moving mirror. The moving head requires the whole of the lamp housing to pan and tilt, whereas the moving mirror has the lamp housing fixed and operates with a motorised mirror in front of the lens. |

Moving Lights: These fall: into two types, moving head and moving mirror. The moving head requires the whole of the lamp housing to pan and tilt, whereas the moving mirror has the lamp housing fixed and operates with a motorised mirror in front of the lens.

MSR: Medium Source Rate Earth type of discharge lamp often used in modern Followspots (see page 26).

Multiplex: See DeMultiplex

Ohms Law: The calculation by which the amperage load of a circuit may be found. N.B. the calculation shown in this book is actually the 'power train calculation' whereas Ohms Law is a slightly different thing. However the calculation shown is widely accepted and named as Ohms Law (see page 45).

Pan and Tilt: The act and ability to swivel and angle the lantern.

PAR: Parabolic Aluminised Reflector. One of the five main categories of lanterns (see page 19).

Peak: The opposite of Flat Field adjustment in a Profile lantern, when a central hot spot may be desired within the image.

Plotting: The work of setting up different lighting states and the method of changes between them, the plotting session being a critical part of the lighting job.

Preset Control: The older more basic type of lighting control desk, providing duplicate faders giving the ability to preset lighting states (see page 52).

Prism Convex Lantern (PC): One of the five main categories of lanterns (see page 18).

Production Desk: Desk/position, usually within the auditorium, being the operational centre during technical set up and rehearsals (see page 64).

Profile: One of the five main categories of lanterns (see page 15).

Prompt Book: Copy of the script/libretto set out to contain notation for all technical actions/cues.

Ray Light: Reflector used in PAR lanterns, producing a very narrow angle beam.

Reflector:	of many different types – all lanterns have a reflector behind the lamp to enhance and improve the light output.
Rigging:	The act of rigging is the placement of lanterns / equipment, usually at high level (see page 57).
Rig Plan:	Large paper plot, showing the layout and detailed information of all lanterns (see page 36).
Safety Bond:	The modern replacement for the safety chain, providing a secondary safety suspension (see page 23).
Shutter:	Within a Profile lantern, one of a set of four shutter blades, used to shape the beam of light.
Spill:	Unwanted elements of light, often associated with Fresnel lanterns, sometimes controlled by the use of a Barn Door.
SWL:	Safe Working Load, SWL labels and notices are found on many pieces of raise and lower equipment and suspension points (see page 59).
Stencil:	Scale representation of lantern shape/types, used in drawing rig plans. Modern CAD packages are now becoming more widely used than the old fashioned stencil.
Tabs:	Or Tableau curtains. These may be the main proscenium arch curtains, often called House Tabs, or a pair of curtains crossing the stage at any position.
Trunion Arm:	Also know as the Yoke, it surrounds the lantern and provides the suspension position.
Tungsten Halogen:	A Lamp having a tungsten filament and a halogen gas infil (see page 23).
Wash:	See coverage
Yoke:	See Trunion Arm
Zoom Profile:	The use of two independently movable lenses within a Profile lantern.

FURTHER READING

ABC of Stage Technology, Francis Reid
ISBN: 0 7136405503   A & C Black   £9.99

ABC of Theatre Jargon, Francis Reid
ISBN: 1 904031 09 9   Entertainment Technology Press   £9.95

Discovering Stage Lighting, Francis Reid
ISBN: 0 240 51545 5   Focal Press   £20.99

Stage Lighting for Theatre Designers, Nigel Morgan
ISBN: 1 904031 19 6   Entertainment Technology Press   £17.95

Stage Lighting Step-by-Step, Graham Walters
ISBN: 0 7136 4639 X   A & C Black   £14.99

The Stage Lighting Handbook, Francis Reid
ISBN: 0 7136 5396 5   A & C Black   £15.99

ENTERTAINMENT TECHNOLOGY PRESS

FREE SUBSCRIPTION SERVICE

Keeping Up To Date with

Basics
A Beginner's Guide to Stage Lighting

Entertainment Technology titles are continually up-dated, and all major changes and additions are listed in date order in the relevant dedicated area of the publisher's website. Simply go to the front page of www.etnow.com and click on the BOOKS button. From there you can locate the title and be connected through to the latest information and services related to the publication.

The author of the title welcomes comments and suggestions about the book and can be contacted by email at:
basics@etnow.com

Titles Published by Entertainment Technology Press

ABC of Theatre Jargon *Francis Reid* **£9.95**
This glossary of theatrical terminology explains the common words and phrases that are used in normal conversation between actors, directors, designers, technicians and managers.

Aluminium Structures in the Entertainment Industry *Peter Hind* **£24.95**
Aluminium Structures in the Entertainment Industry aims to educate the reader in all aspects of the design and safe usage of temporary and permanent aluminium structures specific to the entertainment industry – such as roof structures, PA towers, temporary staging, etc.

Basics - A Beginners Guide to Stage Lighting *Peter Coleman* **£9.95**
Basics introduces newcomers to the world of stage lighting. It will not teach the reader the art of lighting design, but will teach beginners much about lanterns, dimmers, control systems, lamps, electrical safety, etc. and is packed with good, common sense advice.

The Exeter Theatre Fire *David Anderson* **£24.95**
This title is a fascinating insight into the events that led up to the disaster at the Theatre Royal, Exeter, on the night of September 5th 1887. The book details what went wrong, and the lessons that were learned from the event.

Hearing the Light *Francis Reid* **£24.95**
This highly enjoyable memoir delves deeply into the theatricality of the industry. The author's almost fanatical interest in opera, his formative period as lighting designer at Glyndebourne and his experiences as a theatre administrator, writer and teacher make for a broad and unique background.

Introduction to Rigging in the Entertainment Industry *Chris Higgs* **£24.95**
An Introduction to Rigging in the Entertainment Industry is a practical guide to rigging techniques and practices and also thoroughly covers safety issues and discusses the implications of working within recommended guidelines and regulations.

Focus on Lighting Technology *Richard Cadena* **£17.95**
This concise work unravels the mechanics behind modern performance lighting and appeals to designers and technicians alike. Packed with clear, easy-to-read diagrams, the book provides excellent explanations behind the technology of performance lighting.

Lighting for Roméo and Juliette *John Offord* **£26.95**
John Offord describes the making of the production from the lighting designer's viewpoint - taking the story through from the point where director Jürgen Flimm made his decision not to use scenery or sets and simply employ the expertise of Patrick Woodroffe.

Lighting Systems for TV Studios *Nick Mobsby* **£35.00**
Lighting Systems for TV Studios is the first book written specifically on the subject and is set to become the 'standard' resource work for the sector.

Lighting Techniques for Theatre-in-the-Round *Jackie Staines,* **£24.95**
Lighting Techniques for Theatre-in-the-Round is a unique reference source for those working on lighting design for theatre-in-the-round for the first time.

Lighting the Stage *Francis Reid* **£14.95**
Lighting the Stage discusses the human relationships involved in lighting design – both between people, and between these people and technology. The book is written from a highly personal viewpoint and its 'thinking aloud' approach is one that Francis Reid has used in his writings over the past 30 years.

Practical Guide to Health and Safety in the Entertainment Industry
Marco van Beek **£14.95**
This book is designed to provide a practical approach to Health and Safety within the Live Entertainment and Event industry. It gives industry-pertinent examples, and seeks to break down the myths surrounding Health and Safety.

Production Management *Joe Aveline* **£17.95**
Joe Aveline's book is an in-depth guide to the role of the Production Manager, and includes real-life practical examples and 'Aveline's Fables' – anecdotes of his experiences with real messages behind them.

Rigging for Entertainment: Regulations and Practice Chris Higgs **£19.95**
This book expands and develops the subjects covered in *An Introduction to Rigging in the Entertainment Industry*, in particular regulations and safety, rigging practices and equipment.

Sixty Years of Light Work *Fred Bentham* **£26.95**
This title is an autobiography of one of the great names behind the development of modern stage lighting equipment and techniques.

Sound for the Stage *Patrick Finelli* **£24.95**
Patrick Finelli's thorough manual covering all aspects of live and recorded sound for performance is a complete training course for anyone interested in working in the field of stage sound, and is a must for any student of sound.

Stage Lighting for Theatre Designers *Nigel Morgan* **£17.95**
An updated second edition of this popular book for students of theatre design outlining all the techniques of stage lighting design.

Technical Marketing Techniques *David Brooks, Andy Collier, Steve Norman* **£24.95**
Technical Marketing is a novel concept, recently defined and elaborated by the authors of this book, with business-to-business companies competing in fast developing technical product sectors.

Theatre Engineering and Stage Machinery *Toshiro Ogawa* **£30.00**
Theatre Engineering and Stage Machinery is a unique reference work covering every aspect of theatrical machinery and stage technology in global terms.

Model National Standard Conditions *ABTT/DSA/LGLA* **£20.00**
These *Model National Standard Conditions* covers operational matters and complement *The Technical Standards for Places of Entertainment*, which describes the physical requirements for building and maintaining entertainment premises.

Technical Standards for Places of Entertainment *ABTT/DSA* **£30.00**
Technical Standards for Places of Entertainment details the necessary physical standards required for entertainment venues.